CONTENTS

Introduction

Units

Blackline Masters

Using Ginn Geography

Components of Ginn Geography, Year 3

Teachers' Resource Book
Pupils' Books: *Our School* *Shopping* *Weather*
Group Discussion Book

Teaching units and the Pupils' Books

This **Teachers' Book** is divided into teaching units. For each pupils' book, there are two units. Each unit contains background information and activities (see **Figure 1**, opposite). The units provide a framework for organizing work. For *Our School*, the activities have been divided into those relevant to work on local and contrasting school areas (Unit 1) and those looking at a school area in a developing country (Unit 2). *Shopping* also covers local and contrasting areas (Unit 3); Unit 4 looks at a range of shopping issues. These include environmental issues such as recycling; travelling to the shops and the nature of supply and demand; shopping in an economically developing country (Brazil) and how we obtain goods from other countries around the world. The teaching units for *Weather* are organized into activities which involve the children in simple forecasting and observation of the weather (Unit 5) and those which look at weather further afield (Unit 6).

The Blackline Masters

There are sixteen **Blackline Masters** (see pages 49-64). While some are specific to activities for either the school area, shopping or weather, others, particularly the outline maps, could be used in conjunction with any of the books. Outline maps of the UK and the world are included, in addition to maps of some of the locations studied in the **Pupils' Books**.

The Group Discussion Book

The photographs in the **Group Discussion Book** have also been broadly grouped into three groups: one group for each pupils' book. As with the **Blackline Masters**, some photographs will obviously have relevance for more than one of the titles. The **Group Discussion Book** will help supplement and extend activities arising from the **Pupils' Books**. A variety of locations are shown in the photographs. In some cases, these are the same as those studied in the **Pupils' Books**. For example, the photograph of a modern shopping centre (Milton Keynes) can be contrasted with that of a market town (Marlborough). These can be used to supplement a study of those locations in *Shopping*. Sometimes other locations are shown. Markets in Brazil are contrasted with markets in the UK in *Shopping*. The children's understanding of markets in other developing countries can be extended by a study of the West African market scene in the **Group Discussion Book**.

Year	Teachers' Resources	Pupils' Resources
3	**Teachers' Resource Book** Units: 1. Local and contrasting school areas 2. A school area in a developing country	**Pupils' Books** *Our School*
	3. Shopping in local and contrasting areas 4. Shopping issues	*Shopping*
	5. Weather around the school 6. Weather around the world	*Weather*
	Group Discussion Book	
4	**Teachers' Resource Book** Units: 1. Investigating journeys 2. Investigating transport	**Pupils' Books** *Transport*
	3. The water around us 4. The land around us	*Water and the Land*
	5. Life in Shanghai 6. Life in Rio	*Life in Other Countries*
	Group Discussion Book	

Figure 1. Components of Ginn Geography, Key Stage 2, Years 3 and 4

Using Ginn Geography

Ginn Geography strands

Six **Ginn Geography** 'strands' have been identified for Years 3 and 4. These are:

Earth, land and water
Weather and climate
Population and settlements
Economic activities
Communications and movements
Environmental geography

As can be seen from **Figure 2** (opposite), these relate to Attainment Targets 3-4: Physical, Human and Environmental Geography. Attainment Targets 1 and 2 (Geographical Skills and Knowledge and Understanding of Places) are covered throughout all the resources in **Ginn Geography**. The skills specified in AT1 are developed through all the **Pupils' Books** and can be supplemented by the **Group Discussion Book**. For example, the skill of identifying features on aerial photographs can be developed through looking at aerial views of urban and rural school areas in *Our School*, a retail park in *Shopping* and the contrasting urban and rural areas in the **Group Discussion Book**.

Focus of Pupils' Books

Each book has a main focus, which relates to a **Ginn Geography** strand. For example, the main focus of *Weather* is 'Weather and Climate'. However, one of the features of **Ginn Geography** is the interrelationship between the titles. Activities and materials in one can often by supported by material in another. Because of this, each title may cover other **Ginn Geography** strands. The main focus of *Shopping*, for example, is 'Economic Activities', but the material is also relevant for work looking at 'Population and Settlements'. The skill of 'Planning a route' can as easily be developed through a journey to school as a journey to the shops; an understanding of the land use involved in building a superstore can be furthered by looking at the land use around the school. The length and time of journeys are affected by the weather; the structure of a school or shop is also affected by the climatic conditions in a particular place.

A study of the environment can arise most directly from activities related to *Shopping*. Material on recycling is included and the information on the location of superstores can also be used to raise environmental issues. *Our School* includes material on land use and work on the environment can arise through a study of this, particularly when contrasting urban and rural locations.

ATTAINMENT TARGETS →		AT3 Physical Geography		AT4 Human Geography			AT5 Environmental Geography
GINN GEOGRAPHY STRANDS →		Earth, land and water	Weather and climate	Population and settlements	Economic activities	Communication and movements	The environment
PUPILS' BOOKS	*Our School*			[Main focus]	✓	✓	✓
	Shopping			✓	[Main focus]	✓	✓
	Weather	✓	[Main focus]	✓			

[shaded] Main focus of the Pupils' Book

✓ Also covered

Figure 2. Attainment Targets coverage: Physical, Human and Environmental Geography

Key ideas and skills

At the beginning of each teaching unit (see pages 19-48), there is an Activity Summary chart. The activities are grouped into topics for ease of reference. The topics chosen are those which are most relevant to each book. In addition, each activity has a title, so the nature of the work to be undertaken can be clearly seen.

For each activity, one or two 'Key ideas' have been specified. These relate broadly to the Programmes of Study in the National Curriculum. For example, a land use survey (see Unit 1) will help develop the key idea that there is a relationship between land use, buildings and human activities. The activity of tracing a route will help the children understand that people make journeys of different lengths. The activity summary chart from Unit 1 is shown below, as an example.

Activity summary

Activity	Key ideas	Skills
Buildings 1. Looking at homes 2. Land use survey 3. How buildings are used	Homes can be classified according to type; land is used in different ways; the use of buildings can change	Identify features on aerial and other photographs; use letter/number co-ordinates to locate features on a map
Journeys 4. Tracing a route 5. Traffic survey 6. Describing a journey	People make journeys of different lengths; Places are linked by routes	Follow a route using a plan; make a map of a short route; use a large-scale map
Work 7. Job survey 8. Goods and services 9. Town and country jobs	Land use and activities vary between rural and urban areas; People move homes for different reasons; goods and services are provided in different ways	Use geographical vocabulary to talk about places; follow a route using a plan

In addition to the 'Key idea', a skill has been specified, relating to AT1. For example, the land use survey mentioned above will help the children develop the skill of using letter and number co-ordinates. By tracing a route, they are learning how to follow a route by using a plan. The skills that each group of activities develop are shown in **Figure 3**, opposite.

	ATTAINMENT TARGET 1: GEOGRAPHICAL SKILLS	Activities (topic group)		
		OUR SCHOOL	SHOPPING	WEATHER
LEVEL 2	2a Use geographical vocabulary about places	Work Home and school Rich and poor	Local shops Goods from other countries	Forecasting Hot and cold countries
	2b Make a representation of a real or imaginary place		Shopping in the country	
	2c Follow a route using a plan	Journeys Work	Shopping in the country	
	2d Record weather observations made over a short period			Recording the weather
	2e Identify familiar features on photographs and pictures	Buildings	Local shops Superstores	Effects of/ adapting to the weather
LEVEL 3	3a Use letter/number co-ordinates to locate features on a map	Buildings Home and school	Local shops	Hot and cold countries
	3b Use a large-scale map to locate their own position and features outside the classroom	Journeys		Recording the weather
	3c Make a map of a short route, showing features in the correct order	Journeys	Shopping in the country Supply and demand	
	3d Identify features on aerial photographs	Buildings	Superstores The environment	

Figure 3. Attainment Target coverage: Geographical skills

Knowledge and understanding of places

At Years 3 and 4, pupils must study the local area, a contrasting locality in the UK and a locality in an economically developing country. **Figure 4** (opposite) shows the locations studied in the Year 3 and 4 **Pupils' Books**.

Local and contrasting areas

The local area could be defined as anywhere within about 15 minutes walking time, in all directions, from the school gate. For many schools, the locality is an urban or suburban area with a mixture of land uses. Other schools may be in an area with a lot of different housing types, but little variety in land use. The definition of the local area for rural schools is usually easy – it is the village or parish.

The local area is potentially a most important educational resource. In the past, this has often not been recognized by primary schools. Opportunities should be taken for investigating:

- the school buildings and the people who work in or visit the school
- the school grounds – ponds, wild-flower areas, play areas
- weather, including temperatures in and around the school
- where people work
- the relationships between buildings, land use, and human activities
- journeys and transport.

If your school is in an urban area, a rural area would obviously provide the clearest contrast, and vice versa for rural schools. Most urban schools are within an hour's coach drive of a rural or semi-rural area. A visit to a village would be a good starting-point for a geographical study. For children at a rural school, a visit to the shopping centre of a large city would provide a useful starting-point.

Our School provides material on Blackburn in Lancashire and St Abbs in Berwickshire, Scotland. These are two contrasting urban and rural areas. Both are investigated from the starting-point of the school and the area around it.

Shopping contrasts Milton Keynes in Buckinghamshire with Marlborough in Wiltshire. Milton Keynes provides a good example of a place with modern, planned, shopping facilities. Marlborough is an example of an old market town. Similar towns to Milton Keynes and Marlborough could be selected from the local area, using the material in *Shopping* as a basis for investigations. The material on Caldbeck in Cumbria provides another example of shopping in a rural locality.

Details on all the above places can be found in the Background Information sections at the beginning of each unit.

In *Weather*, the 'local' area is effectively the school. The children are encouraged to observe and record weather changes in their immediate locality and to think about how these affect them.

	Local and contrasting areas in the UK	Localities in economically developing countries	Pupils' Book
YEAR 3	Blackburn, Lancs St Abbs, Berwickshire, Scotland	India: Chembakolli	*Our School*
	Caldbeck, Cumbria Marlborough, Wilts Milton Keynes, Bucks	Brazil: Imperatriz	*Shopping*
YEAR 4	Churchtown, nr Southport The Lake District Liverpool Saltaire, nr Bradford	India: Delhi	*Transport*
	The Cheviot Hills The Fens The Pennines The Rivers Severn and Thames	Brazil: The Amazon	*Water and the Land*
		Brazil: Rio China: Shanghai	*Life in Other Countries*

Figure 4: Locations covered in Year 3 and Year 4 Pupils' Books

Localities in an economically developing country

The world can be divided according to the relative wealth of each country. The rich countries are variously called the Rich World, the First World, the Advanced Western Nations or the North. The former Communist Bloc states of Eastern Europe and the USSR were classified as the Second World. Poorer countries, mainly in tropical and sub-tropical parts of South America, Africa and Asia have variously been called the Third World, the Poor World or the South. The current description for the poorer parts of the world is 'economically developing countries'.

Children of primary school age should be made aware of the diversity of people and places in the world. It can be a problem trying to engage their interest in people and places in distant countries. *Our School* was devised with this in mind. Material is provided on Chembakolli in India. This can be supplemented by the Action Aid pack (see Useful addresses, page 18). By taking the school as the starting-point, the children's interest will be engaged. Schools, land use, buildings, work and journeys in Chembakolli can all be compared with those in the UK locations. Climatic conditions are also mentioned: this could provide a useful supplement to the activities in *Weather.* It is important that the children also have insight into developments in *urban* parts of India. The material in *Our School* could be supplemented by a study of a city location, such as Delhi.

Shopping looks at markets and other forms of shop in Brazil. The pages on 'Food from around the world' can be used prior to investigating some of the different countries who export food to the UK.

Talking about weather changes could lead to an investigation of the problems faced by economically developing countries. Can these be linked to climatic conditions? What role do the charities play in assisting these countries. *Shopping* provides information on charities which could supplement activities originally stimulated by material in *Weather.*

Teaching Geography

Planning Geography

Geography is concerned with stimulating the children's curiosity about the world. Geographical investigations enable them to become more aware of their environment and to make sense of the world in which they live. By becoming engaged in geographical and environmental activities, children will be prompted to ask questions, to investigate and to enquire. This obviously needs careful preparation and planning.

In the planning stage, there need to be clearly identified tasks which will develop increased knowledge and understanding of geography. Geography is a good subject for prompting questions and encouraging enquiring minds.

The investigative approach

High standards of achievement in geography are associated with problem-solving and investigative approaches and a combination of whole class, individual and group work. Resources such as those provided in **Ginn Geography** – maps, plans, aerial and other photographs provide opportunities for this. These resources are supplemented by a questioning approach in the text and activities.

Questions

Throughout the **Pupils' Books**, the children are encouraged to look at the maps, plans and photographs to find particular features and then talk about what they observe. Questions are included throughout, to develop an investigative approach.

These questions can be broadly divided into two categories, as shown below.

1. 'Where, who and what . . .?'

These are questions which encourage definitions and descriptions. Where are Blackburn, St Abbs and Chembakolli? What are their most important natural and people-made features? Who lives there? Throughout **Ginn Geography**, the emphasis is on making comparisons so, the natural progression from these questions is 'In what ways is this place similar or different from where we live?'. Children are being encouraged to observe, measure and look for patterns.

2. 'How and why . . .?'

How did this place become like this? Why is this factory, office or supermarket block here? Information collected in geography can both provide answers to these questions and stimulate further enquiry. The children should be encouraged to think about the past and the future. How did the grid pattern of the streets develop in Milton Keynes? Why? Why does Marlborough have such a wide High Street?

The children should also be encouraged to express their personal feelings about a place. Would they like to live there? Could it be improved?

Activities

The purpose of the activities in the **Pupils' Book** is to give ideas for things to do, stimulated by the subject matter of the particular pages that they appear on.

For example, this activity in *Our School* encourages the children to develop their own skill in following directions, based on the example they have seen:

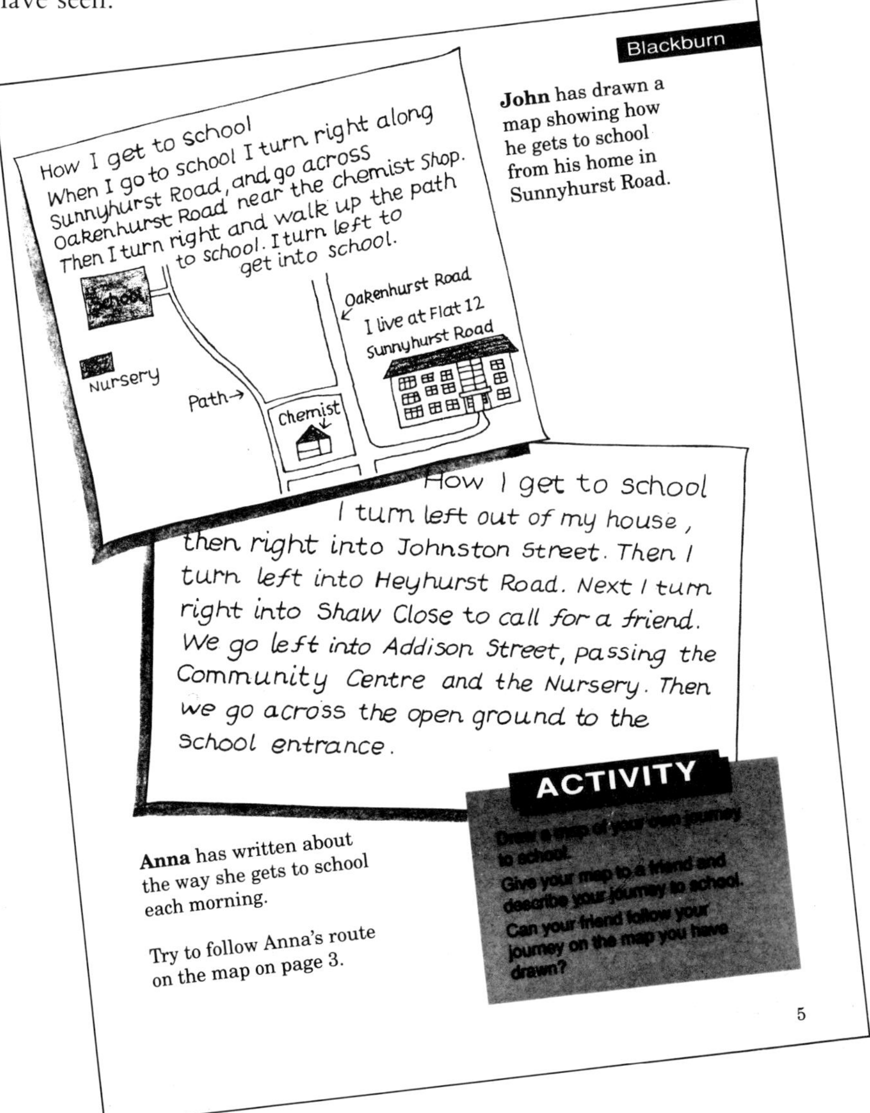

Blackburn

John has drawn a map showing how he gets to school from his home in Sunnyhurst Road.

How I get to school
When I go to school I turn right along Sunnyhurst Road, and go across Oakenhurst Road near the chemist shop. Then I turn right and walk up the path to school. I turn left to get into school.

How I get to school
I turn left out of my house, then right into Johnston Street. Then I turn left into Heyhurst Road. Next I turn right into Shaw Close to call for a friend. We go left into Addison Street, passing the Community Centre and the Nursery. Then we go across the open ground to the school entrance.

Anna has written about the way she gets to school each morning.

Try to follow Anna's route on the map on page 3.

ACTIVITY

Draw a map of your own journey to school.
Give your map to a friend and describe your journey to school.
Can your friend follow your journey on the map you have drawn?

5

This **Teachers' Book** includes these activities. These are indicated by the words 'activity' box alongside the relevant **Pupils' Book** page. It also provides a wide variety of additional activities.

Map and fieldwork

Map and fieldwork skills are best built into on-going geography work rather than being done in isolation. It is useful to collect a range of maps, including large-scale Ordnance Survey maps. Simple orienteering exercises around the school buildings and grounds are particularly good for developing map skills. Many of the activities in the **Pupils' Books** and this **Teachers' Book** will help develop such skills. The use of alpha-numerate co-ordinates is encouraged wherever applicable and the children have the opportunity to develop their understanding of scale and distance. This can range from the use of simple plans – for example, following a shopper's route around a superstore (in *Shopping*) to using a street plan (in *Shopping* and *Our School*).

Cross-curricular elements

The National Curriculum specifies cross-curricular dimensions, skills and themes. These dimensions, skills and themes can be promoted through the variety of activities included in **Ginn Geography**.

Cross-curricular dimensions

The dimensions should be concerned with providing all pupils with equal opportunities and education for life in a multi-cultural society, irrespective of ability, race or gender. They are at the very centre of every aspect of the curriculum both taught and 'hidden'. By providing positive images from a range of locations and cultures in the UK and abroad, **Ginn Geography** encourages pupils to be culturally aware and tolerant members of society.

Cross-curricular skills

These skills are the basic skills which should be developed throughout the curriculum through a range of experiences:

1. Communication skills: oracy,
literacy,
numeracy,
graphicacy.
2. Problem-solving skills
3. Study skills
4. Personal and social skills
5. Information technology.

Activities involving map reading, following routes and giving directions will help develop communication and problem-solving skills particularly. The use of information technology is encouraged in **Ginn Geography** wherever applicable.

Cross-curricular themes

The themes ensure that children do not only learn 'subjects' within narrowly defined limits. They enable children to experience the overlap which exists between one area and another and to really have a broad, balanced curriculum. They include:

1. Environmental Education
2. Economic and Industrial Understanding
3. Citizenship
4. Health Education
5. Careers Education and Guidance.

The first three of these themes are particularly relevant to geographical work.

Assessment

The **Ginn Geography** materials are carefully structured to allow progression in children's learning. As was explained earlier (pages 2-10), they are related to National Curriculum Programmes of Study and Statements of Attainment, so that planning for classroom activities can be undertaken with assessment outcomes clearly in mind.

Planning for assessment

The **Ginn Geography** materials offer a clear progression of activities across the different year levels. Teachers may wish to select particular themes and activities to cover aspects of the Programmes of Study, planning necessary resources and assessment opportunities: **Blackline Master 16** can be used for this.

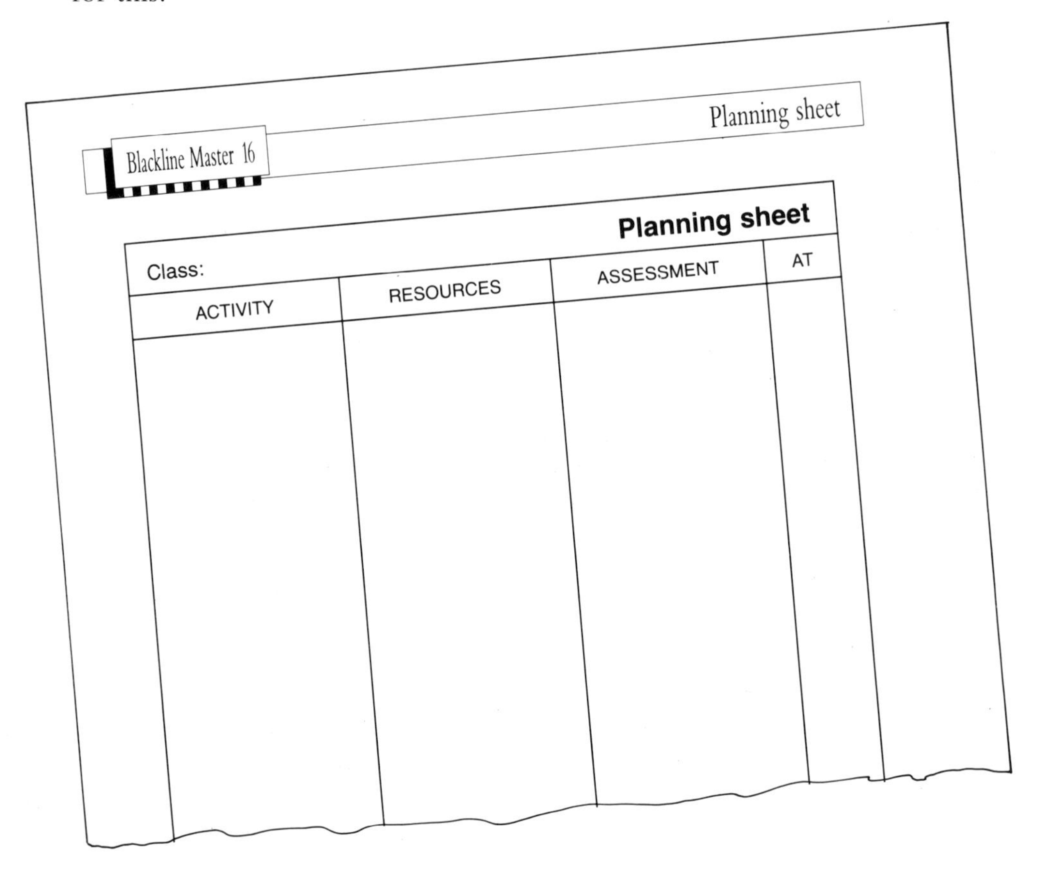
Blackline Master 16 — Planning sheet

Planning sheet

Class:

ACTIVITY	RESOURCES	ASSESSMENT	AT

An alternative planning mechanism would be to break down each activity into knowledge and skills relating to the Attainment Targets:

ACTIVITY: *Investigating superstores*			
Knowledge	AT	*Skill*	AT
Describe uses of land and buildings in the local area	*AT2 2(b)*	*Identify features on aerial photographs*	*AT1 3(d)*

Assessment

Classroom observation

The activities in this **Resource Book**, and in the **Pupils' Books**, lend themselves to individual, small group and whole class teaching. These allow the teacher to observe both the process of learning and the assessable outcomes. Focussed observation, targeting perhaps three children in any one session, will allow the teacher to relate planned outcomes to actual results. This will generate information over a period of time. During the course of work on any particular unit, a range of assessment statements will be produced. The teacher should be aware of the difficulty of assessing individuals in group contexts, and should ensure that corroborative evidence for assessment is sought. This could take the form of further observation in a differently-constituted group, or observation of the same group over a period of time engaged on a variety of tasks. The **Blackline Masters** (pages 49-64) offer one source of activity where clear outcomes can be observed and recorded.

Gathering evidence

The nature of the activities suggested means that the children will produce work in many contexts: some will be written, some graphical, some oral, and some a combination of all of these. A simple but rather crude method of tracking progress would be to register completion of particular themes and associated activities on a checklist. However, progress recorded in this way can often be more apparent then real, since checklists give little information about the level of understanding the child has reached. They are relatively simple to complete, but can be very difficult to interpret, producing a mass of data in an indigestible form. They should not be relied upon as the only source of evidence of attainment.

Producing a portfolio of work

A cumulative collection of evidence might be more revealing. This could be in the form of actual work produced by the child. This would demonstrate acquisition of particular skills or significant stages in understanding. A portfolio of work, selected by both child and teacher, and annotated to indicate its significance, is more illuminating than a collection of ticks in boxes, and can form the nucleus of a Record of Achievement. Both child and teacher should have reasonably clear criteria on which to select pieces of work for inclusion in the portfolio:

- what was the context in which the work was produced?
- was it unaided or the result of specific support?
- what was the nature of the task the child was engaged in?
- who has selected the work for the portfolio?
- why is this place of work significant (what learning or progress does it show?)
- does the work indicate a particular level of attainment in terms of the National Curriculum?

This information is most conveniently recorded on a pre-printed sheet which can be attached to the piece of work. Much of the sheet should be completed by the child as an essential stage in self-assessment, with the teacher adding more focussed comments when necessary. Two examples of what such sheets might look like are given below.

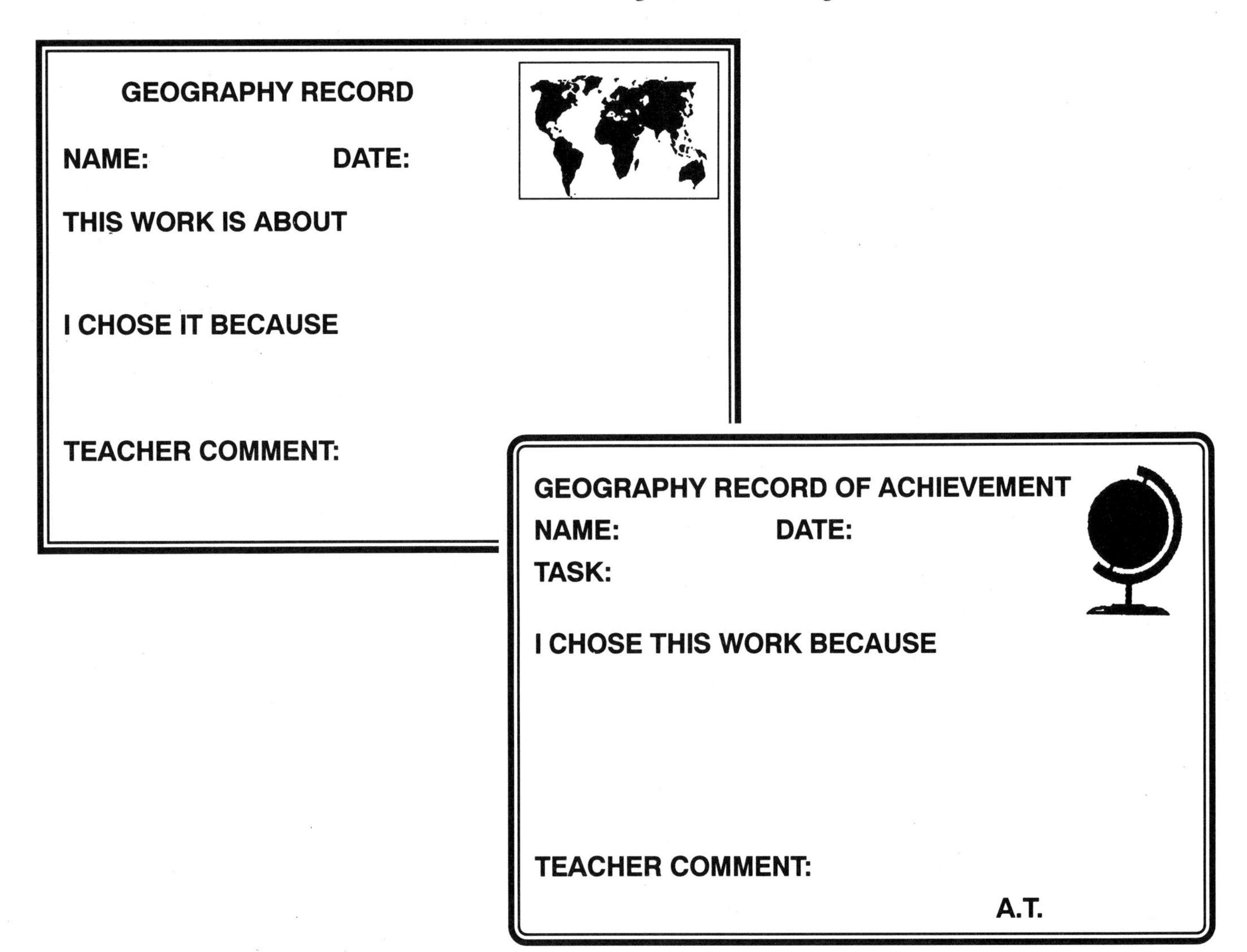
GEOGRAPHY RECORD

NAME: DATE:

THIS WORK IS ABOUT

I CHOSE IT BECAUSE

TEACHER COMMENT:

GEOGRAPHY RECORD OF ACHIEVEMENT

NAME: DATE:

TASK:

I CHOSE THIS WORK BECAUSE

TEACHER COMMENT:

A.T.

If this practice is adopted across the curriculum, it is evident that very quickly a mountain of work will be collected, which could be counter-productive. Too many examples of work will inhibit both child and teacher from using the portfolio as a growing record of achievement. Some pruning of the work collected is necessary to keep the process manageable. It is, therefore, important to build in a review period, so that particular pieces of work can be re-appraised by both child and teacher, and either left in the portfolio as still being significant, or replaced by a more recent example of the child's attainment. Once children are involved in the selection and management of their work, they take great pride in keeping their portfolio in an attractive and usable form. Portfolios, if carefully managed, can provide opportunities for:

- clear planning, with assessment opportunities identified
- careful observation of the learning process
- clear evidence of attainment, which can be annotated.

Figure 5 (opposite) summarizes the Attainment Targets that are covered by **Ginn Geography, Year 3**.

Units	AT1 Geographical skills	AT2 Knowledge and understanding of places	AT3 Physical geography	AT4 Human geography	AT5 Environmental geography
1. Local and contrasting school areas	2(a), 2(c), 2(e), 3(a), 3(b), 3(c), 3(d)	2(a), 2(b), 2(c), 2(d), 3(b), 3(c), 3(d), 3(e), 3(f)	3(c)	2(a), 2(b), 2(c), 3(a), 3(b), 3(c), 3(d)	2(a), 2(b)
2. A school area in a developing country	2(a), 2(c), 2(e), 3(a)	2(d), 3(d)	3(a)	2(a), 3(b), 3(d)	2(a), 2(b)
3. Shopping in the local area	2(a), 2(b), 2(c), 2(e), 3(a), 3(c), 3(d)	2(b), 2(c), 2(d), 3(c), 3(d), 3(e), 3(f)	3(c)	2(b), 2(c), 3(b), 3(c), 3(d)	2(b)
4. Shopping issues	2(a), 3(c), 3(d)	2(b), 2(c), 2(d), 3(c), 3(d)		2(b), 2(c), 3(c), 3(d)	2(a), 2(b), 2(c), 3(a), 3(b)
5. Weather around the school	2(a), 2(d), 2(e), 3(b)	2(a), 2(c), 2(d)	2(a), 2(b), 3(b)	2(b)	
6. Weather around the world	2(a), 2(e), 3(a)	2(c), 2(d), 3(d)	3(a)	3(a), 3(b)	2(b)

Figure 5. Correlation chart between activities in the units and National Curriculum Attainment Targets

Useful addresses

Our School

Suppliers of aerial photographs

Aerofilms Limited
Gate Studios, Station Road,
Borehamwood, Herts WD6 1EJ

Central Register of Air Photography for Wales
Cartographic Services,
(P56), Welsh Office,
Room G-003 Crown Offices,
Cathays Park, Cardiff CF1 3NQ

Geonex Jasphot Ltd
92-94 Church Road,
Mitcham, Surrey CR4 3TD

Jeffersons Air Photography
Hangar 1, Liverpool Airport (North),
Speke, Liverpool L24 1YD

Ordnance Survey
Air Photo Sales, Romsey Road, Maybush,
Southampton SO9 4DH

Skyscan
Oak House, Toddington, Cheltenham,
Glos. GL54 5BY

Charities and development agencies

Action Aid
Hamlyn House, Archway,
London N19 5PO
Action Aid produce a teachers' pack *Chembakolli – a village in India*. This contains colour photographs, a map, a story, notes and background information. It is available from Action Aid at the following address:
The Old Church House, Church Steps,
Frome, Somerset BA11 1PL

Christian Aid
PO Box 100, London SE1 7RT

National Association of Development Education Centres
6 Endsleigh Street, London WC1H 0DX

Oxfam
274 Banbury Road, Oxford OX2 7DZ

Save the Children Fund
Mary Datchelor House, 17 Grove Lane,
Camberwell, London SE5 8RD

Shopping

Computer programs

'Datashow'
This program will allow pupils to enter up to eight items of data, and sort them numerically or alphabetically. They can then see this displayed in a table, bar chart, or pie chart.

'Touch Explorer Plus'
This can be used with a concept keyboard to stimulate discussion about the changing uses of buildings over time. An overlay map of the immediate locality around the school can be made and information about it stored.

Available from:
NCET, Unit 6,
Sir William Lyons Road,
Science Park, Coventry,
West Midlands CV4 7EZ

Environmental organizations/ companies supplying recycling information

British Glass (Recycling Dept)
Northumberland Road,
Sheffield S10 2UA

The British Paper Board and Industry Federation
3 Plough Place, Fetter Lane,
London EC4A 1AL

Friends of the Earth (England)
26-28 Underwood Street, London N1 7JA

Friends of the Earth (Wales)
3 St James Street, Porthcawl,
Mid Glamorgan CF36 3BG

Friends of the Earth (Scotland)
15 Windsor Street, Edinburgh EH7 5LA

Other information

Town plans are available from:
Goad Plans, Chas E. Goad Ltd,
Salisbury Square, Old Hatfield,
Herts AL9 5BJ

For further information on Milton Keynes:
Milton Keynes Development Corporation
Saxon Court, 502 Avebury Boulevard,
Central Milton Keynes, Bucks MK9 3HS

Weather

Equipment suppliers

Philip Green Educational
112a Alcester Road, Studley,
Warwicks B80 7NR

NES Arnold
Ludlow Hill Road, West Bridgford,
Nottingham NG2 6HD

Philip and Tacey Ltd
North Way, Andover,
Hampshire SP10 5BA

Other information

Investigating Weather by C. B. Green and R. M. James (published by Arnold-Wheaton). Provides general information on the weather.

UNIT 1 LOCAL AND CONTRASTING SCHOOL AREAS

Ginn Geography resources

Pupils' Book *Our School*

Related Pupils' Books *Shopping*
Transport (Year 4)

Group Discussion Book pages 2-9

Blackline Masters 1, 3, 4, 6, 7

2 per week ? or link as want.

Activity summary

Activity	Key ideas	Skills
Buildings 1. Looking at homes 2. Land use survey 3. How buildings are used	Homes can be classified according to type; land is used in different ways; the use of buildings can change	Identify features on aerial and other photographs; use letter/number co-ordinates to locate features on a map
Journeys 4. Tracing a route 5. Traffic survey 6. Describing a journey	People make journeys of different lengths; Places are linked by routes	Follow a route using a plan; make a map of a short route; use a large-scale map
Work 7. Job survey 8. Goods and services 9. Town and country jobs	Land use and activities vary between rural and urban areas; People move homes for different reasons; goods and services are provided in different ways	Use geographical vocabulary to talk about places; follow a route using a plan

Background information

Blackburn

Blackburn has been chosen as an example of an urban area for contrast with St Abbs, a rural area. It is a town of approximately 140,000 people in Lancashire in the North West of England. It is served by a railway link with Bolton and Preston and is well placed on the North West motorway network. The Leeds to Liverpool Canal runs through the town. Much of the older housing stock that was built in the 19th century has been cleared. There is now a mixture of housing. There are traditional streets of stone and brick terraces, low-rise and high-rise flats built in the 1960s and modern estates of both municipal and private housing. The town centre redevelopment began at the end of the 1960s and continues into the 1990s. With the decline of the cotton trade, a wide range of industry is now evident with former cotton mills being converted to other uses. Immigration from Commonwealth countries (mainly India, Pakistan and Bangladesh) began in the 1960s. There is a particular link with the Gujerat region of India, and Gujerati is the most common language amongst the Asian-origin population.

St Abbs

St Abbs is a small fishing village of about 300 people on the east coast of Scotland. It is centred on its harbour, from where a fleet of in-shore fishing boats operates. Most of the adult males of St Abbs are occupied in the fishing industry, either going fishing in small boats owned by themselves or by local syndicates or crewing on the larger ocean-going vessels operating from nearby Eyemouth. Many women in the village work in the fish-processing factories on the quayside at Eyemouth. Other work in the area includes farming, wildlife conservation and the tourist industry. St Abbs Head is the site of a bird sanctuary of international importance. Like many other small and picturesque villages, St Abbs is popular with second-home owners and is therefore at risk of depopulation. At the time of writing, the village school has only six children.

Glossary

demolished, detached, graze, loch, reservoir, quarry, quay, sanctuary, semi-detached, settlement, terraced, tide.

Activities

Resources

Buildings

1. Looking at homes

Our School
pages 4, 6-7 (activity box), 8-9, 10

Group Discussion Book
pages 8, 9, 22

Blackline Master 7

Make a list of the sorts of homes that the children in the class live in. The photographs in **Our School** can be used to show the different types of housing: flats, semi-detached, detached, terraced. The children can make a graph like the one on page 7 of **Our School** to show these. **Blackline Master 7** can be used to compare homes and other aspects of life in Blackburn, St Abbs and Chembakolli.

Different types of housing can be located on the aerial photographs on pages 8-9 of the **Group Discussion Book**. The photograph of the Canadian house on page 22 can be used as the starting-point for discussing the relationships between building materials, styles of house, climate and location.

2. Land use survey

Our School
pages 8-9

Group Discussion Book
pages 7, 8, 9

Blackline Master 3

On pages 8-9 of **Our School** the children are asked to prepare their own chart showing the land use around the school, colour coded accordingly. If aerial photos of your school are available (see Useful addresses, page 18), use these to identify and plot the different uses, divided into simple categories: services, industry, housing, shops, etc. A land use chart of the Blackburn map on page 2 can be made by tracing **Blackline Master 3** and colouring in the different uses.

The photograph of farming on page 7 of the **Group Discussion Book** can be used as a stimulus to discussing land use in a rural area.

3. How buildings are used

Our School
pages 4, 7
See also **Shopping**

Arrange a trip to an area in your locality with a good mixture of different building styles. Ask the children to list the different types of building they see and to note down how the buildings are being used now and how they think they were once used. Keep a note of any unusual features: old stables, mews, courtyards. This could be combined with work done in connection with **Shopping** (see Unit 3, activity on Shop Signs).

Journeys

4. Tracing a route

Resources

Our School
pages 2, 5 (activity box)

Blackline Masters 3, 4

Using **Blackline Master 3**, the children can trace the journeys described on page 5 of **Our School**. Ask them to plot alternative routes and look for reasons why the children use the routes that they do. **Blackline Master 4** can be used in a similar way to trace routes in St Abbs.

Using large-scale maps of the area around your school, follow this up by ask the children to plot journeys made by themselves, eg:
- children's journeys to school
- routes to the nearest town
- routes taken for shopping (in immediate neighbourhood and to shopping centres, supermarkets, etc.)

Introduce directional terms – left/right, north/south/east/west.
Using a written or recorded version of someone else's journey to school, try to follow it on a map.

5. Traffic survey

Our School
pages 3, 11
See **Shopping**
See also **Transport** (Year 4)

Group Discussion Book
pages 8, 9

The roads shown on the maps of Blackburn and St Abbs can be compared and contrasted. Which roads are the two places served by? Are there any motorways nearby? Are there likely to be any traffic problems in the two places?

Conduct a traffic survey of a road near your own school. The children can then make graphs to show:
- amount of traffic at different times of day
- types of traffic
- the direction in which the traffic is going.

Are there obvious reasons why the amount of traffic varies at different times?

Find out where your town or village is in relation to major routes. Where is the nearest motorway? Which centres does it connect? Is your school on an A route, a B route, or a minor road?

Investigate the car parks in the area. Why are they there? Are they free or is there a fee? Careful use of interview and survey techniques as people return to their cars can establish whether most traffic using the car park is local or has come from elsewhere.

6. Describing a journey

Our School
page 5
See also **Transport** (Year 4)

Ask the children to describe their own journeys to school:
- in words, speaking to a friend
- in words, written down
- in pictures
- on tape
- in a diagram
- using a pictorial map
- using a conventional map.

Which of these is easiest to follow? Why? How can different features such as roads or buildings or parks be shown on a map? Look at a range of maps: compare the use of symbols and of colour. What conventions do most map-makers follow?

Find out how many children come to school on foot, by car, by bus or train. Make graphs to show the results.

Resources

Work

7. Job survey

Our School
pages 8-9, 12-13, 14-15
See also **Shopping**
Life in Other Countries
(Year 4)

Carry out a class survey of parental occupations (sensitivity to domestic circumstances may be required). List the different kinds of job. Discuss how they differ from the kinds of jobs available in either Blackburn or St Abbs. How many parents work in manufacturing industries; in tourism or recreation; in offices; in service industries; in shops?

Do both mothers and fathers go out to work? Make graphs of the results.

There may be a major employer in your town or village, where many of the children's parents work. Find out more information on the company and the sorts of goods and services they supply.

You could also find out how many of the children's parents work close to home or further away. Use a smaller scale map to plot the distances travelled by parents to get to work. Is there any link between this and the results of your traffic survey?

8. Goods and services

Our School
pages 8-9, 12-13 (activity box)
See also **Shopping**

Group Discussion Book
pages 8, 9

Blackline Master 6

Look at the things produced by industries and businesses in your town or village. Discuss why they are produced there. Where do they go once they have been made? Are there any international contacts?

Find out where everyday foodstuffs come from: tea, coffee, vegetables, fruit, bread, fish, meat, milk, canned goods, frozen foods, etc. **Blackline Master 6** can be used to trace the production of coffee, from the plant to the packets in the shops. There are obvious links here with **Shopping** (see Units 3-4).

Look at service industries such as those connected with tourism and recreation. Is there anything in your town or village which people come to visit? Does this provide work for local people? What effect do visitors have on life in the community? Ask the children to try to see the issue from both positions: as a resident and as a visitor. On page 13 of **Our School** the children are asked to write a tourist guide for St Abbs. This could be followed up by writing a 'tourist guide' for visitors to their own area, emphasizing the positive aspects.

9. Town and country jobs

See also **Shopping**
Transport (Year 4)
Life in Other Countries
(Year 4)

Look at the differences between goods and services produced in a rural area and those produced in an urban area. Discuss the differences. Which 'town' products do people in the country rely on? Which 'country' products do people in the town rely on?

How far do people need to travel in search of work? (see above). Is this easier in a town or in the country? Check the availability of bus and train services in your area, and compare them with those in a contrasting area. Examine the notion of a commuter area. What effect does this have on the life of a rural community?

Arrange an exchange of letters, and possibly an exchange visit, with a school in a contrasting area within the UK. Focus on establishing the similarities and differences between schools, jobs, houses and recreation in each area.

UNIT 2 A SCHOOL IN A DEVELOPING COUNTRY

Ginn Geography resources

Pupils' Book *Our School*

Related Pupils' Books *Shopping*
Weather
Life in Other Countries (Year 4)

Group Discussion Book pages 2-9

Blackline Masters 2, 5, 6, 7

Activity summary

Activity	Key ideas	Skills
Home and school 1. Homes in a hot country 2. Comparing schools 3. Children at work	Localities have features and occupations which are similar to and different from our own	Use geographical vocabulary to talk about places; use letter/number co-ordinates to locate features on a map
Food and farming 4. Food from different countries 5. Stages of producing coffee and tea 6. Visit to a market	Landscape, weather and wealth affect people's lives in economically developing countries	Use letter/number co-ordinates to locate features on a map
Rich and poor 7. Looking at how places change 8. Finding out about charities 9. Similarities and differences	Localities change as a result of human actions	Use geographical vocabulary to talk about places

Background information

Chembakolli

Chembakolli is a remote tribal village in the Nilgiri Hills in the state of Tamil Nadu in Southern India. The people of Chembakolli belong to a hill tribe called the Adivasis, who are outside the traditional caste system of India. The village is surrounded by fields of cash crops – tea, coffee and rice – and subsistence crops. Recent development work in the village, supported by the British relief organization Action Aid, has allowed the people of Chembakolli to start their own savings bank. This is now financing both agriculture and education, and bringing a medical service to the village. Using their savings, the people of Chembakolli have been able to start such projects as a tea nursery, where they can grow tea plants from seedlings bought from larger estates, and a nursery for the youngest children in the village. This has meant that older children, especially girls, can be freed from some of the responsibilities of looking after their younger brothers and sisters, and are able to go to school. The village has an electricity supply, and there is a weekly market and film show in the improvised cinema.

Action Aid have produced an excellent pack of photographs and supporting material on Chembakolli, which would be an invaluable resource in exploring this particular village further. (See Useful addresses, page 18, for details).

The **Ginn Geography** pupils' book **Shopping** has a section on charity shops, which can be used as a supplement for general work on the nature of charities.

Glossary

monsoon, tea, nursery, traditions, tribe.

Activities

Home and school

1. Homes in a hot country

Resources

Our School
pages 16-19 (activity box: 18)
See also **Weather**
Life in Other Countries
(Year 4)

Group Discussion Book
pages 22, 23

Begin by looking at the photographs of Chembakolli in **Our School**. Talk about the houses in the village and compare them with the children's homes. Are the same building materials used? Why is there very little glass evident in the windows? Find out more about houses in India.

Discuss how the building of houses is affected by the weather. Ask the children to make a list of advantages and disadvantages of life in a temperate and sub-tropical climate. Talk about how the weather affects our lives in Britain. As well as housing, consider transport, clothing, health. Compare these aspects with Chembakolli.

The photographs on pages 22 and 23 of the **Group Discussion Book** show different types of houses in hot and cold countries.

2. Comparing schools

Our School
page 16
See also
Life in Other Countries
(Year 4)

Group Discussion Book
pages 2, 3

Blackline Master 7

Compare the photographs of schools in Chembakolli and other developing countries (See **Group Discussion Book**, page 3) with your own school. What are the similarities and the differences? Consider particularly: buildings, facilities, materials, journeys to school (see **Group Discussion Book**, page 2), number of children in the class, age at which children begin and leave school, etc. Ask the children to write and draw pictures about the differences.

Discuss why education matters in a remote region of a developing country. What sorts of skills do the children need? Talk about the language and traditions of the area.

Blackline Master 7 can be used to compare schools, homes and journeys in Blackburn, St Abbs, Chembakolli and the local area.

3. Children at work

Our School
pages 16, 18, 20-21
See also
Life in Other Countries
(Year 4)

Discuss what it means to be a child in a developing country: caring for younger brothers and sisters to allow parents to work; working in the fields when extra hands are needed; unequal access to both education and health care; long journeys to school and to work across difficult terrain. Compare this experience with the life of a child in the UK.

How many of the children in the class work in the home, perhaps for pocket money? What kinds of jobs do they do? How do these compare with the children of Chembakolli?

Life in Other Countries gives information about the lives of children in China and Brazil, and includes material on the jobs done by poor children in Rio.

Resources

Food and farming

4. Where does food come from?

Our School
pages 20, 21 (activity box)
See also **Shopping, Life in Other Countries** (Year 4)

Blackline Master 2

Ask the children to bring wrappers and labels from basic foodstuffs, especially tea, coffee and rice, to school. Plot the countries of origin on **Blackline Master 2** (outline map of the world). Discuss similarities in climate and economic status.

The children can then try to work out what conditions are necessary to allow these crops to be grown. Work linking with Science can be undertaken to test ideal growth conditions for seeds, and to identify the essential factors of the growth medium, water, light and heat. Talk about how conditions are different for farmers in the UK and farmers in India.

Cash crops are grown in Chembakolli to provide income. Which crops are grown for food? How are these different to the food crops we grow in this country?

5. Stages of producing tea and coffee

Our School
pages 20, 21
See also **Shopping**

Blackline Master 6

Talk about the process which leads from coffee plant or tea bush to a packet on a supermarket shelf, pointing out the many people involved along the way, and the increasing value as the basic commodity is processed, packed and sold. Development education agencies (see Useful addresses, page 18) have devised games to simulate the trade between developed and under-developed countries.

Look at the other side of the relationship: those commodities which are produced in the industrial world and exported to developing countries. Do the same economic factors apply?

How many items in the children's daily lives are imported? From which countries? Do any of their parents manufacture products which are exported to other countries?

6. Visit to a market

See **Shopping**

Group Discussion Book
pages 11, 12, 13

Blackline Master 2

Arrange a visit to a local market. Make lists of the range of goods available, especially in the food market. How many of them are basic foodstuffs and how many could be considered as exotic or luxury items? Compare this with a market in a developing country. Are there any goods from India?

Collect wrappers from a fruit stall to indicate countries of origin. Plot on a map of the world (**Blackline Master 2**). Find out how this produce reaches Britain.

There are photographs of markets in **Shopping** (pages 5 and 19) and the **Group Discussion Book** (pages 11, 12 and 13).

This activity can be linked with a similar one undertaken for **Shopping** (see Unit 3).

Resources

Rich and poor

7. Looking at how places change

Our School
page 20

Talk about the savings bank which the villagers of Chembakolli have set up to organize and fund projects in the village. Why is it necessary? When do we need to save? What for? Explore the idea of many small contributions combining to fund a major development. Team games and activities can contribute to the idea of strength in unity.

Set up a simulation to explore priorities for example, equipping a ship to set sail across an ocean, or filling a rucksack prior to climbing a mountain: what is essential, what are the constraints, what is a luxury, what are the consequences of choice? Children could work in groups to explore ideas and make decisions, and then report back to defend their choices. Computer software (see Useful addresses, page 18) is available for this kind of simulation.

8. Finding out about charities

Our School
pages 16-21
See also **Shopping, Weather**

Investigate the work of relief agencies such as Action Aid (see Useful addresses, page 18), to discover the kind of support offered internationally to developing countries. Follow the process through from the collecting tin/ flag day to improvements on the ground. It is important to avoid the danger of stereotyping: developing countries are not always passive recipients of aid, but, as is proved by the Chembakolli case study, can devise mechanisms and systems for self-help.

What do the relief agencies provide which a developing country cannot? (The emphasis has changed in recent years, from direct financial support to advice and manpower to implement change). How do the children think they can help?

9. Similarities and differences

Our School
pages 22-23 (activity box)
See also
Life in Other Countries
(Year 4)

Blackline Master 7

On pages 22-23 of **Our School**, the children are encouraged to imagine themselves as three of the children in Blackburn, St Abbs and Chembakolli. Organize the class into groups, of three and give them a list of questions to ask about the three places. They can take it in turns pretending to be from one of the three locations. As a follow-up, ask them to think of more questions to add to the list to ask about their own area.

UNIT 3 SHOPPING IN THE LOCAL AREA

Ginn Geography resources

Pupils' Book *Shopping*

Related Pupils' Book *Our School*

Group Discussion Book pages 10–17

Blackline Masters 1, 8, 9, 10, 11

Activity summary

Activity	Key ideas	Skills
Local shops 1. Survey of local shops 2. Classifying shops and services 3. Visiting a general store 4. Looking at shop signs 5. How shops change	Land and buildings are used in different ways in the local area; some shops sell goods while others provide services	Use geographical vocabulary; identify familiar features on photographs and pictures; use letter/number co-ordinates to locate features on a map
Superstores 6. Investigating shopping areas 7. Building superstores 8. Shopping survey	Localities change as a result of human actions; modern shopping locations and environments are carefully planned	Identify features on an aerial photograph
Shopping in the country 9. A walk round Caldbeck 10. Looking at country services 11. Market towns	Some goods and services are provided locally while others are not; some settlements have distinctive features which reveal their function or origin	Follow directions; follow routes; measure straight line distances; make a representation of a real or imaginary place

Background information

Marlborough

Malborough is a very old market town in Wiltshire. It is said that Merlin is buried at the castle mound, the oldest part of the town and now part of Marlborough College. Many battles were fought there during the Civil War. Buildings were destroyed in two fires in the seventeenth century. This means that most of the older half-timbered houses are hidden in the small back lanes off the high street. Marlborough is on the main road between London and Bristol and so historically has been an important market town.

Milton Keynes

Milton Keynes is a purpose-built 'new town', built in the 1960s. The roads have been built in a grid pattern. All the shopping areas have been planned and most of this area is pedestrianised.

More information on Milton Keynes can be obtained through the Development Corporation (see Useful addresses, page 18).

Caldbeck

Caldbeck is a small village situated under the Northern Fells of the Lake District. There is a primary school, several small craft shops and the shops mentioned in **Shopping**. The location of Caldbeck within the Lake District National Park should be emphasized.

Other information

Shopping centres are being built everywhere. They will only be located in an area if it fulfils the following four criteria:

1. The land area must be large enough: 5 acres and above
2. There must be enough space to develop a large car park and if possible a petrol filling station
3. Sites must have good access to an uncongested highway
4. The sites in question must have commercial viability – be near areas of high population and be accessible.

The trend with Tesco and other superstores has been to favour edge-of-town sites for the location of new stores. However, Tesco also take advantage of derelict land, believing that this often improves the surrounding environment. Old buildings may be taken over and remodelled in character with the surrounding areas. In Lewisham, for example, the store has been built on the site of a derelict brewery bottling plant. Old railway properties in Mold and Northwhich, a redundant bus garage in East Didsbury and a former steel works in Bidston Moss are all urban renewal projects which have been carried out. Stores may also be sited within existing listed buildings.

Critics of edge-of-town sites for superstores believe that these take people away from the city centre stores. Advocates of the out of town centres argue that they reduce traffic congestion in city centres and make them pleasanter places to shop, especially where the city centre has been pedestrianised.

Glossary

customers, goods, mobile shop, parade, pawnbrokers, pedestrianised, scanning, second-hand, service, refrigerated, retail park.

Activities

Resources

Local shops

1. Survey of local shops

Shopping
pages 2, 3, 7

Walk to the shops near your school. Ask the children to note down the types of shops and what they sell. This will lead to names being given to different sorts of shops. A graph can then be made to show which shop is the most common. You could use the computer program 'Datashow' to do this (see Useful addresses, page 18).

A classification for the types of shops near your school can be devised or use the one in **Shopping** (page 7). As an extension for more able pupils, look at ways of breaking this down into different types of food shops.

2. Classifying shops and services

Shopping
pages 6-7

Shops can be divided into those which sell goods and those which provide a service: hairdresser; bank; estate agent. Find out where the parents of the children in your class go to obtain these services. This could be conducted as a survey and the results either graphed or marked on a sketch map of the area around the school. Discuss why there are fewer services in less-populated areas.

3. Visiting a general store

Shopping
pages 3, 8, 18-19

Visit the nearest general store or corner shop to the school. Find out how long it has been there. Ask the children to make a list of the things are sold there. Can they buy these things in their local supermarket or superstore?

The children can record this information in a variety of ways – by taking photographs, drawing and painting, graphs and written accounts.

The poem 'General Store' on page 3 of **Shopping** can be used as a stimulus to talking about such shops in other countries. The photograph of the general store in Brazil (pages 18-19) can also be used to provide a comparison.

See Unit 4, page 36, for a related activity.

4. Looking at shop signs

Shopping
page 2

The photographs on page 2 of **Shopping** show the hairdressers' and the pawnbrokers' symbols. Have the children ever seen these symbols before? Ask them to look for signs on the fronts of local shops. Discuss how, in the days before most people could read, many shops had signs and symbols to tell customers what they sold. This activity could be done in conjunction with 'How buildings are used' (see Unit 1, page 21).

As a follow-up, ask the children to design some shop signs themselves.

Resources

Local shops cont'd

5. How shops change

Shopping
page 9 (activity box)

On page 9 of **Shopping**, the children are asked to find out about the history of their local shops. This can be done by talking to shop owners, parents and grandparents.

The computer program 'Touch Explorer Plus' (see Useful addresses, page 18), can be used for this activity.

Superstores

6. Investigating shopping areas

Shopping
pages 4, 10-11

Group Discussion Book
pages 10, 11

Blackline Master 8

Using **Blackline Master 8**, ask the children to locate the roundabout, woodland area and petrol station on the aerial photograph on page 4 of **Shopping**. Ask them to write about how they think the area looked before the superstore was built. As a follow-up, work can be done on areas where shopping has been carefully planned. The photographs on pages 10-11 of the **Group Discussion Book** can be used for contrast here.

7. Building superstores

Shopping
pages 14-15

Why are stores located in particular places? Ask the children to list the advantages and disadvantages of the location of their nearest superstore.

A chart like this one could be made to show this:

The best place for a superstore

Name of store	Location town centre/ out of town	Advantages	Disadvantages	Other features
Tesco	out of town	near a roundabout used up waste land	gets very busy very long queues at the tills	area very clean now

You could write to a local store for a plan of the inside of the store, like the one on pages 14-15 of **Shopping**.

Resources

Superstores cont'd

8. Shopping survey

Blackline Master 11

Carry out a survey, using **Blackline Master 11**, of the shopping habits of the children's family. The children are asked to select the shop that is visited most frequently, which may be a large superstore. Follow this up with some more general questions:
– Who does the shopping in your family?
– How do they travel to the shops?
This work can be followed up with activities undertaken in **Transport** (Year 4).

Shops in the country

9. A walk round Caldbeck

Shopping
pages 8-9

Blackline Master 9

Using the plan of Caldbeck (**Blackline Master 9**) ask the children to mark the route from the farm to the village store and the Third World shop. A return route, via the footpath along the river from the church can be marked. The children can then work out how far they walked altogether.

Looking at **Blackline Master 9**, can the children find any evidence to suggest that Caldbeck is a tourist area? (For example, the hotel and gift shop). Ask them to locate these features by giving a grid reference.

10. Looking at country services

Shopping
pages 8-9

If your school is in a rural area, ask the children to make a list of the local services. How far are these from the school? Are there any services which have been cancelled recently? The children could make a list of the advantages and disadvantages of living in a rural area.

If your school is in an urban area, ask the children to find out more about Caldbeck, or a similar village which they may have visited on holiday or on a field trip. Make maps and plans of the chosen places.

11. Market towns

Shopping
pages 10-11

Group Discussion Book
page 11

Marlborough is a good example of an old market town. The photographs in **Shopping** and the **Group Discussion Book** can be used as a basis for discussing such towns. Find out the nearest market town to the school. Why did it become a market town? When is market day? Look at the shape and pattern of the streets. Market towns often have a wide main street with a brick built Guild Hall or similar building at the end. Why is this? Comparisons could be drawn between Marlborough and the local market town.

UNIT 4

Ginn Geography resources

Pupils' Book *Shopping*

Related Pupils' Books *Our School*
Transport (Year 4)
Life in Other Countries (Year 4)

Group Discussion Book pages 10–17

Blackline Masters 2, 6, 11

Activity summary

Activity	Key ideas	Skills
Supply and demand 1. Travelling to the shops 2. Mobile shopping 3. Price survey	People make journeys of different lengths; goods and services are provided in different ways	Measure straight line distances; make a map of a short route
Goods from other countries 4. Food from around the world 5. Shopping in Brazil 6. Charity shops	Goods in our shops come from different countries; landscape, weather and wealth affect lives in a developing country.	Use geographical vocabulary to talk about places
The environment 7. Protecting the environment 8. Recycling chain 9. Making paper	Human activities change the environment; some activities are designed to improve the environment	Identify features on aerial photographs

Background information

Brazil

Brazil has a population of 147 million, most of whom live near the coast. There are great contrasts between the lifestyles of the rich and poor: more than two-thirds of the population live below poverty level. Nevertheless, the economy of Brazil is a powerful one. Coffee, rubber, gold, iron ore and soya beans are all important exports.

Brazil has one of the largest areas of rainforest in the world. Over the years, vast areas of the forest have been destroyed to make way for huge iron ore, logging and aluminium smelting complexes. These have been required for the opening of the Transamazonia Highway by the Brazil Government. As the forests are cleared, people are settling there.

The particular, location mentioned in **Shopping** is Imperatriz. Once a village, Imperatriz is now a city of ½ million people. There are very few services. The small farmers have no land and are forced, like the Gonzales family mentioned in **Shopping**, to move into favelas (shanty towns). The living conditions are very bad. There is air pollution caused by the saw mills. Infant mortality is very high, with 85 deaths (of children under 5) out of 1,000. The infant mortality rate in the UK is 11 deaths out of 1,000. Life expectancy is 65 years, compared with 75 years in the UK. Only 1 child in 10 stays at school until the age of 10 years. Many adults can not read and write, due to the inadequate provision of secondary and higher education.

There is more information on Brazil, specifically Rio de Janeiro, in **Life in Other Countries** (Year 4).

Other information

The activities on recycling in this unit will help the children be aware of the importance of safeguarding the environment.

On pages 22-23 of **Shopping**, the process of recycling glass is shown. The recycling of glass is important because:

- it cuts down the quarrying of sand and limestone
- it saves space in landfill sites
- it saves on the energy needed to quarry, process and deliver raw materials
- it saves on energy at the glassworks.

Glass is made by melting together sand, limestone, soda ash and waste glass. The recycling centres like to keep the three colours separate, because of their varying degrees of purity.

The large superstore chains can be a good source of information on recycling and other environmental topics.

Glossary

charity, famine, recycling, saw mills.

Activities

Resources

Supply and demand

1. Travelling to the shops

Shopping
pages 12-13

Group Discussion Book
page 10

Blackline Master 11

Carry out a class survey to find out where the children's parents travel to buy a range of different products: furniture, electrical items, clothes for special occasions, gifts for Christmas and birthdays etc. On an area map, mark where they travel to, and ask the children to work out distances from home. This can supplement work arising from pages 12-13 of **Shopping**.

Blackline Master 11 (Shopping Survey) can be used to note down distances travelled to the shops and the form of transport used).

2. Mobile shopping

Shopping
pages 12-13

On page 12 of **Shopping**, the children are asked whether they have ever bought anything from a shop on wheels. Discuss the obvious ones – ice-cream vans, hamburger/hot dog vans etc. If you live in a country area, find out which mobile shops visit the area and who uses them. The photograph of a water seller in Brazil, on page 12, can also be used as a stimulus.

3. Price survey

Shopping
pages 3, 18-19

Ask the children to find out the price of six basic items from their nearest grocer or corner shop. Then ask them to find out the prices of the same items from the local supermarket or superstore. Make a graph showing the differences. Discuss why there are differences in prices.

Talk about 'general stores' and the role they play in supplying a wide range of everyday needs. See Unit 3, page 31, for a related activity.

Goods from other countries

4. Food from around the world

Shopping
pages 16-17 (activity box)

Group Discussion Book
pages 12-13

Blackline Master 2

Use **Blackline Master 2** to refer to pages 16-17 in **Shopping** for this activity. The children can mark the countries mentioned on these pages on the outline. They could do this by drawing the relevant fruit or vegetable on the map.

Repeat this activity with other goods sold in the shops. Some goods have less well-known countries of origin, and by looking these up the children can develop skills in using an atlas.

Resources

Goods from other countries cont'd

5. Shopping in Brazil

Shopping
pages 12-13

There are photographs of three different types of shop in Brazil on pages 12-13 of **Shopping**. These can be used as a stimulus for discussing the different sorts of goods that are sold, and how the shops compare with shops in the UK.

As a follow up, there is more material on Brazil in **Life in Other Countries** (Year 4).

6. Charity shops

Shopping
pages 20-21 (activity box)

Group Discussion Book
pages 14-15

Blackline Master 2

Visit a local charity shop and collect leaflets and other information on the countries that are being helped. Ask the children to mark these countries on **Blackline Master 2** (outline map of the world).

On page 21 of **Shopping**, the children are asked where some Oxfam products come from and to locate these on a map of the world. This could be extended by finding out about the origins of similar goods in the charity shops' catalogues. Pages 14 and 15 of the **Group Discussion Book** show craft workers in Thailand and Bangladesh. These photographs can be used to show the children the source of the goods they see in shops like Oxfam, and to discuss the nature of traditional crafts.

The environment

7. Protecting the environment

Shopping
pages 4, 22-23

Group Discussion Book
page 16

Blackline Master 8

Visit a local superstore to investigate its commitment to preserving the local environment. Ask the children to collect the store's leaflets about this and note which goods are in recycled packages, which have been made from recycled materials, etc.

This can be extended to looking at the area around the store. Start by looking at the aerial photograph on page 4 of **Shopping**. Ask the children to note the surroundings and discuss which aspects are environmentally friendly/unfriendly. Mark these on **Blackline Master 8** (outline of the Sandhurst shopping area).

Resources

The environment cont'd

8. Recycling chain

Shopping
pages 22-23

Group Discussion Book
pages 16-17

See pages 22-23 of **Shopping**, which show the glass recycling process. Make a simple, illustrated chain of pictures to show this process from beginning to end, e.g.

1. Drinking a bottle of coke
2. Taking the bottle to the bottle bank
3. Bottle bank to lorry
4. Journey to recycling centre
5. Process of crushing at the recycling centre
6. Production of new bottle
7. New bottle on supermarket shelf

For more information on recycling, contact the addresses listed in Useful addresses, page 18.

The photographs on pages 16-17 of the **Group Discussion Book** show paper, glass and can banks at a store, and a glass crushing plant.

9. Making paper

Shopping
page 23 (activity box)

Making re-cycled paper is an interesting activity for the children.

1. First, you need a rectangular sieve with a detachable frame called a deckle. These can be bought at art shops or you can make one of your own.

Use eight pieces of wood, each of the same length, to make two identical frames. Secure the frames with nails and waterproof glue. Stretch a fine mesh over the top and sides of the frames, and secure with drawing pins. The mesh could be made from an old net curtain. Put the frame with the mesh (the sieve) beneath the one without (the deckle).

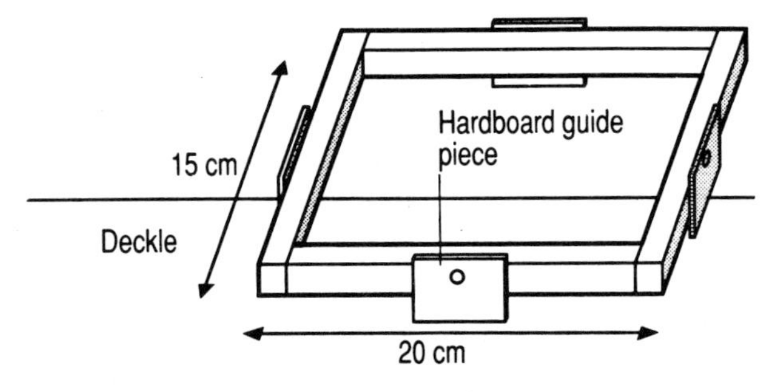

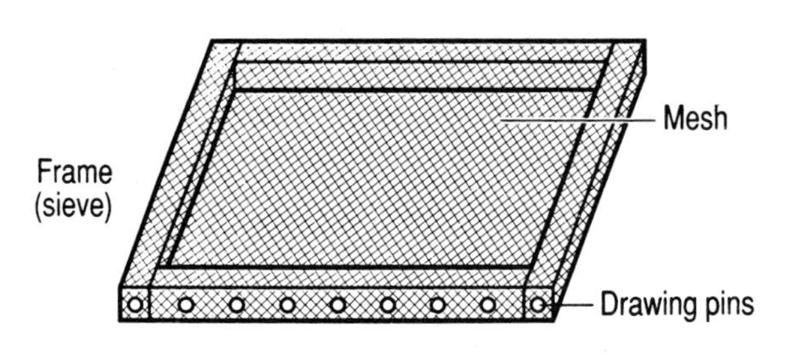

2. Tear up paper into small pieces and soak overnight in warm water. Add washing-up liquid to remove ink. Squeeze and mash up the paper in a bowl large enough to fit the frame and deckle. The pulp will be like porridge when you have added half a bowl of warm water.

3. Place a bowl underneath deckle and frame, or put over a sink. Pour the pulp over the mesh and smooth it out.

Take a flat piece of wood or hardboard to fit within the frame, to act as a press. Place on the pulp and weight it down. Leave for a few days until dry.

UNIT 5 WEATHER AROUND THE SCHOOL

Ginn Geography resources

Pupils' Book *Weather*

Related Pupils' Books *Our School*
Water and the Land (Year 4)
Life in Other Countries (Year 4)

Group Discussion Book pages 18-24

Blackline Masters 1, 13, 14, 15

Activity summary

Activity	Key ideas	Skills
Forecasting the weather 1. Weather symbols 2. Weather sayings 3. Looking at clouds 4. Shipping forecasts	Information on the weather can be presented and used in different ways	Use geographical vocabulary; identify familiar features on photographs and pictures
Recording the weather 5. Daily weather record 6. Collecting weather data 7. Making a wind rose 8. Temperatures around the school	Site conditions can influence surface temperatures and affect wind speed and direction	Record weather observations over a short period; measure and record weather using direct observation and simple equipment; use large-scale maps
The effects of the weather 9. Weather poems and pictures 10. Extreme weather conditions 11. Changing seasons 12. Weather colours	The seasons have different weather patterns; weather affects us in different ways	Identify familiar features on photographs and pictures

Background information

Resources and equipment

Useful addresses (page 18) gives details of places to contact for equipment to undertake simple forecasting and recording. It may also be useful to make links with other educational institutions – sixth-form colleges, polytechnics, etc. to help with resourcing. These can often help by, for example, loaning expensive equipment such as a satellite receiver.

Recording the weather

The pupils' book **Weather** includes simple instructions for making a wind rose, a windsock, a simple anemometer (to measure wind speed) and a rain gauge). It should be remembered that, to achieve accurate measurements, wind and rainfall need to be recorded on open ground away from the main school buildings. Weather forecasters use the 'Beaufort Scale' to measure wind forces. These forces range from Force 0 to Force 12 (hurricane). Some of these forces are illustrated on page 19 of **Weather**. (The term 'hurricane' is discussed in the background information to Unit 6).

Temperatures on different sides of a school building, in the soil, at ground level, and in the air, all vary. A thermostruck thermometer is a useful resource as it can measure temperature in soil, water, or air.

It is useful to record information collected on the weather onto a computer database. It can then be recalled, added to, sorted and exchanged with other schools.

Glossary

forces, forecasters, forecasts, humidity, prevailing wind, radiosonde balloon, recorded, sunrise, sunset, visibility.

Activities

Resources

Forecasting the weather

1. Weather symbols

Weather
pages 8-9

Blackline Masters
1, 13, 15

Ask the children to design their own symbols to show the weather: sun, wind, rain, cloud, hail, snow. Video a weather forecast. Look at the symbols. Are they the same or different from the children's? Discuss why we need conventional symbols. **Blackline Master 15** shows the standard symbols. These can be cut out and stuck onto an outline map of the UK (**Blackline Master 1**). From information given on the television forecast, the children could record the hottest, coldest, wettest and driest places in the UK on a particular day. (**Blackline Master 13** can be used for this).

2. Weather sayings

Talk about weather sayings and rhymes. Are there any local ones? The children could then write these down and illustrate them. These could be used as an alternative form of weather forecasting. How accurate are they compared with conventional methods?

3. Looking at clouds

Weather
pages 14-15 (activity box)

Group Discussion Book
page 24

On page 14 of **Weather** there are photographs of the three main types of clouds. The children can observe and draw the clouds passing by the classroom windows. What sort of weather do they think is on the way? Are there heavy, grey, rain clouds or high, puffy, clouds?

The photograph on page 24 of the **Group Discussion Book** shows heavy rainclouds at night.

4. Shipping forecast

Weather
page 8
See also **Our School**

Blackline Master 12

Blackline Master 12 shows the sea areas around the UK which are mentioned in the shipping forecasts on the radio. Tape a shipping forecast for the children to listen to. **Blackline Master 12** can be used to locate the places mentioned. The children can then look these up in an atlas. St Abbs is often mentioned in shipping forecasts. See **Our School** for more information on the village and the fishing industry.

Resources

Recording the weather

5. Daily weather record

Weather
pages 8-9 (activity box)

Blackline Masters 14, 15

Record the weather with the conventional symbols two or three times a day. The weather symbols on **Blackline Master 15** can be cut out and pasted onto a graph or chart. Then look back to see how many times each weather condition or element was recorded. The children could then make simple charts to see how many times the different conditions have occurred during a particular month or season. **Blackline Master 14** can also be used to keep a general daily record of weather conditions.

6. Collecting weather data

Weather
pages 10-11, 20-21

Group Discussion Book
page 18

Contact another local school and exchange weather data regularly. Fax the data at a set time each day or send by post. Compare the results – are they similar to yours? Why? Also compare a school further away, perhaps in a contrasting locality in the UK or in another country. Is there a local weather station to visit or from which you can obtain information? Put any data onto a simple database and print out graphs and charts comparing different localities, weeks and seasons. Ask the children to look in their altases and see if they can work out why each locality has certain weather conditions. In the **Group Discussion Book** (page 18) there is a satellite image showing weather systems over the Earth. This can be used as a stimulus to discussing how weather data is collected.

7. Making a wind rose

Weather
pages 18-19

Wind direction can be recorded daily on a wind rose. There are instructions for how to make one of these on page 18 of **Weather**. Remember to record the direction the wind is coming *from*.

After recording wind direction for several weeks, the children can work out where the prevailing wind is coming from. Do your records show it comes mainly from the east, north or south west? Look outside and see if there is other evidence to support the findings. Are the trees bent in a particular way? Is the building weathered more on one side than another? Do children nearly always stand in the same place to shelter from the wind? Is there any evidence inside school – can you feel the draught more on one side than another?

8. Temperatures around the school

Weather
pages 22-23

Temperatures around the school will be affected by sun and wind. Some classrooms face south and could be too hot in summer, others could freeze in winter. How do you cope with this in school? Can you shade or open the window, turn the heating up, down or off? Ask the children to find the hottest part of school, the most draughty, the coldest. The children can locate these places on large-scale maps and plans.

Resources

The effects of the weather

9. Weather poems and pictures

Weather
page 3 (activity box)

The poem 'Snowball Wind' on page 3 can be used as a stimulus for children writing and illustrating their own poems about the weather. Reference could be made to famous paintings which show different sorts of weather conditions. As a follow-up, they could write poems and draw pictures or take photographs about other different types of weather conditions.

10. Effects of extreme conditions

Weather
pages 4-5 (activity box), 12-13
See also
Water and the Land (Year 4)

Group Discussion Book
page 24

On a very wet day, ask everyone how they came to school and how the rain generally affected the start to their day. Did they – put on special clothes, wait for the rain to stop, come in a taxi/bus/car instead of walking? How are they affected by other extreme weather conditions – snow, ice, extreme heat – when coming to school? They could make a chart, like the one shown on page 4 of **Weather**. There are photographs of extreme weather conditions on pages 12-13, including material on the 1987 hurricane. This could be used as a starting-point for finding out more about hurricanes.

The photograph of thunder and lightning on page 24 of the **Group Discussion Book** can be used as stimulus to talking about the children's own experience of these conditions.

Water and the Land (Year 4) has useful follow-up material on rain.

11. Changing seasons

Weather
pages 6-7

In the UK, the changing seasons bring changing weather. Talk about the sort of weather the children expect in spring, summer, autumn, winter. Have they any experience of 'unseasonal' weather conditions – a very cold day in the summer, a very mild day in the winter? On pages 6-7 of **Weather** there are examples of some of the different people who need to know about the weather. How might people's jobs change with the seasons, for example, what sorts of work is done on a farm in the different seasons?

12. Weather colours

Weather
pages 15

Ask the children to observe the colours of the sky at different times of the day. What colours can they see? Can they draw pictures to show these colours? Talk about the different colours seen at sunrise and sunset.

UNIT 6 WEATHER AROUND THE WORLD

Ginn Geography resources

Pupils' Book *Weather*

Related Pupils' Books *Our School*
Life in Other Countries (Year 4)
Water and the Land (Year 4)

Group Discussion Book (Year 3) pages 18-24

Blackline Masters 2, 12, 14

Activity summary

Activity	Key ideas	Skills
Hot and cold countries 1. Finding countries in an atlas 2. Living in a cold country 3. A school in a hot country 4. Tropical rainforests	Weather conditions vary in different parts of the world	Use geographical vocabulary to talk about places; use letter/number co-ordinates to locate features on a map
Adapting to the weather 5. How animals adapt 6. Looking at homes 7. Weather and food 8. Weather and leisure	The weather in other localities affects the lives of the people and animals who live there	Identify features on photographs and pictures
Weather dangers 9. Newspaper reports 10. Drought and famine 11. Tornadoes and hurricanes	Extreme weather conditions in different parts of the world can adversely affect people's lives	Use geographical vocabulary to talk about places

Background information

Overseas locations

Information about the weather in specific countries can obviously be found in a variety of secondary sources – books, atlases, TV and newspaper reports. The **Ginn Geography** titles **Our School** (Year 3) and **Life in Other Countries** (Year 4) have weather-related material on India (**Our School**); China and Brazil (**Life in Other Countries**). Primary sources can also be used. Which countries have the children or their parents visited recently? How did the weather affect their stay there? Children from countries other than the UK can also discuss their experiences of these places.

Weather dangers

Material is available in the form of old newspaper reports and books on the 1987 hurricane in the UK. This could be used as the starting-point for talking how the rarity of such extremes in the UK and the frequency of weather dangers in some other countries. A hurricane is a Force 12 wind. It is characterized by a central 'eye'. This is created by the spin of the Earth which causes the winds to circle around the centre. A tornado is characterized by its twisting shape, which is caused by a column of air forming beneath a thunder cloud.

Glossary

drought, hurricane, tornado, tourist.

Activities

Resources

Hot and cold countries

1. Finding countries in an atlas

Weather
pages 2, 12-13, 17

Group Discussion Book
pages 22, 23

Blackline Master 2

Looking at a map in an atlas, ask the children to name:
two countries which are often hot
two countries which are often cold
two countries which have a lot of rain
two countries which are very dry
Are the countries near the Equator or the Poles? Does this have any influence on temperature? Why? The countries can then be marked on an outline map of the world (**Blackline Master 2**).

The photographs of Canada and Oman on pages 22-23 of the **Group Discussion Book** show two clearly contrasting cold and hot.

2. Living in a cold country

Weather
pages 2, 17

Group Discussion Book
pages 20, 21, 22

Investigate life in a cold country. How has the temperature there affected life? Do people or animals live there? How do they keep warm? What are their homes like? The photograph of the Inuit boy on page 2 of **Weather** can be used to stimulate discussion, as can the photographs on pages 20-22 of the **Group Discussion Book**.

3. A school in a hot country

See **Our School**
See also **Water and the Land, Life in Other Countries** (Year 4)

Group Discussion Book
page 3

Look at the photograph of the school near Marabá, in the Amazon Basin on page 3 of the **Group Discussion Book**. Is the school similar to yours or different? How does the weather affect the clothes people wear, the materials used to build the school and whether or not there is any heating? How would children in very cold places be affected, at school, going to school? What they wear?

4. Tropical rainforests

See **Water and the Land, Life in Other Countries** (Year 4)

Group Discussion Book
page 3

Ask the children to find the River Amazon in South America. This area has a tropical climate. There is no shortage of water and there is plenty of sun, too. How do these people live? What do they eat? What clothes do they wear, how do they travel, what kind of houses do they build? Compare this with life in polar and desert places.

Resources

Adapting to the weather

5. How animals adapt

Group Discussion Book
pages 20-21

Look at the photograph of the Arctic fox in winter and summer on pages 20-21 of the **Group Discussion Book**. How has it adapted to the change in weather? Why is it a different colour? Find out about animals in different countries which have become adapted to suit the weather conditions where they live – i.e. yak, camel, seal, polar bear. (Think of polar regions, dry tropical regions, temperate regions and wet tropical regions). How have animals adapted – what are their special features?

6. Looking at homes

See **Our School**

Group Discussion Book
pages 22-23

Start by looking at the photograph of the houses in Canada and Oman on pages 22-23 of the **Group Discussion Books**. Use these to discuss similarities and differences in varying localities. Can the children see how buildings are influenced by the weather? The photographs of Chembakolli in **Our School** can also be used when discussing the nature of buildings and how they are built to stand-up to differing weather conditions.

7. Weather and food

See **Our School, Shopping**

Group Discussion Book
pages 12-13

Blackline Master 2

Using the photographs of markets in the **Group Discussion Book**, talk about fruits which are not grown in the UK. Why are they not grown here? Where are they grown? Can the children say why they are grown there, i.e. what is the weather like to enable them to grow? Find the countries in your atlas and mark them on a world map.

Consider also places where food, and other exports, are grown in advance. Examples might be flowers from Jersey or tomatoes from Guernsey. Why can these be produced before ours in the UK? What fruits and vegetables can we grow in our weather conditions? Can we only eat strawberries in summer? Why?

8. Weather and leisure

Weather
pages 4-5, 17

On page 17 of **Weather**, the tourist industries of Austria and Switzerland are mentioned. Discuss how some countries depend on the snow for their winter sports. What happens when there is not enough snow? Discuss, as a contrast, places which depend on the sun for their tourist industry. Which of our leisure pursuits, such as sports, depend on the weather? (See pages 4-5).

Resources

Weather dangers

9. Newspaper reports

Cut out newspaper reports on the weather. Use a wide variety of papers – the tabloid papers give small amounts of simple information. The *Guardian on Saturday* has a great deal of information relating to the UK, Europe and further afield. This will be too complex to give directly, so give the children one or two extracts, to discuss and question. When there is a major weather disaster, discuss in general terms the country in which this happened, some possible causes, etc. Find out more about how the country is being helped. Talk about how people prepare for and cope with weather problems and how the environment is affected and changed by these.

10. Drought and famine

Weather
page 13
See also **Shopping**

Blackline Master 2

On pages 12-13 of **Weather**, there is a photograph of children collecting water from a well in Burkina Faso in West Africa. This can be used as a stimulus for discussing the problems of drought and famine. What happens in hot and dry countries when there is little water? How do people find water to drink, water crops, wash and cook? Ask the children to look in an atlas to find a hot, desert area. They can then find out more about this area and the problems it might have. A link can be made with work done on charities in **Shopping**.

11. Tornadoes and hurricanes

Weather
pages 12-13

Group Discussion Book
pages 18, 19

The photographs on page 12 of **Weather** show clearly the different shapes of a tornado and a hurricane. Use these as a stimulus for discussion. This can be supplemented by the photographs in the **Group Discussion Book** (pages 18, 19) both showing the eye of a hurricane as a satellite image.

Outline map of the UK

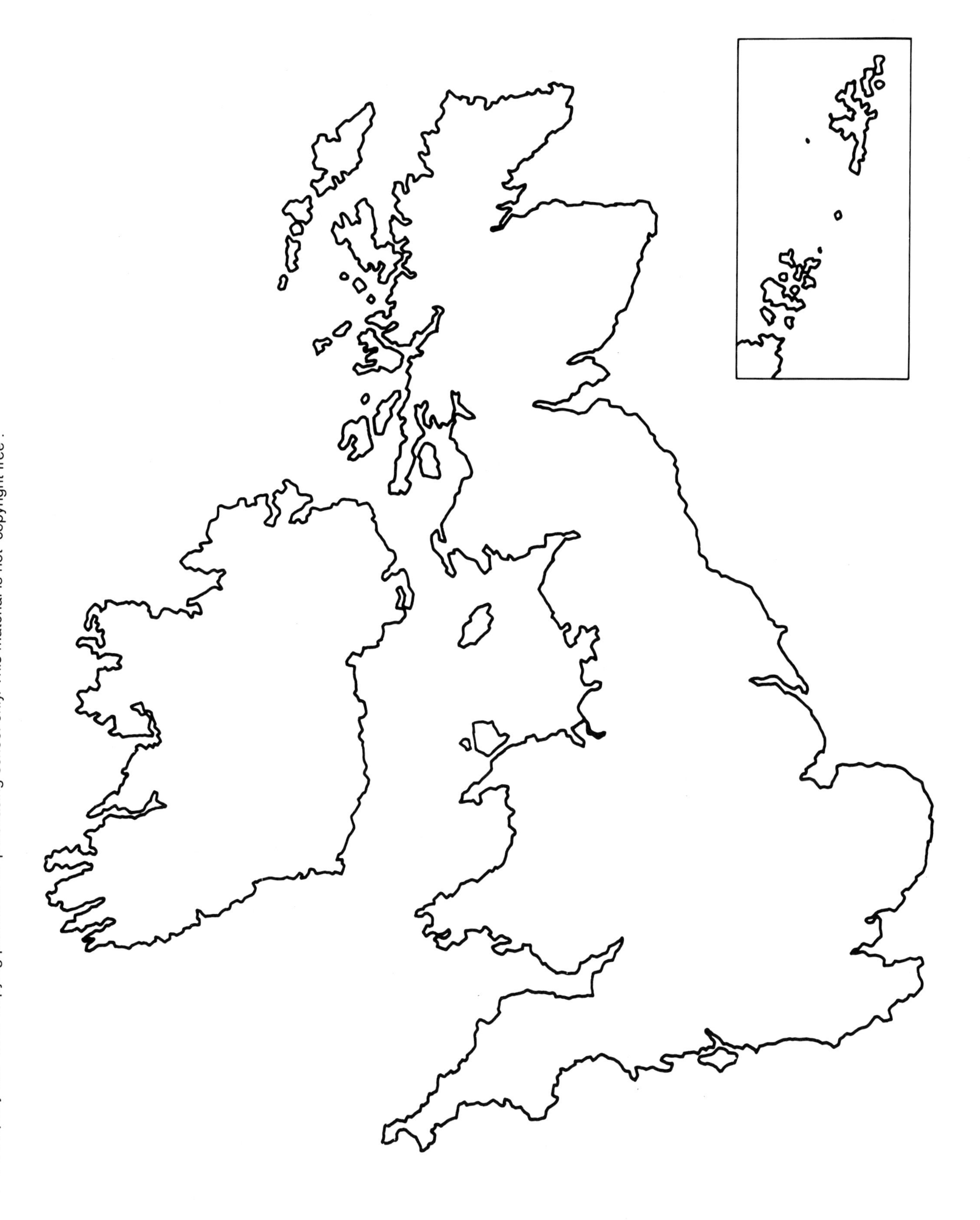

Outline map of the world

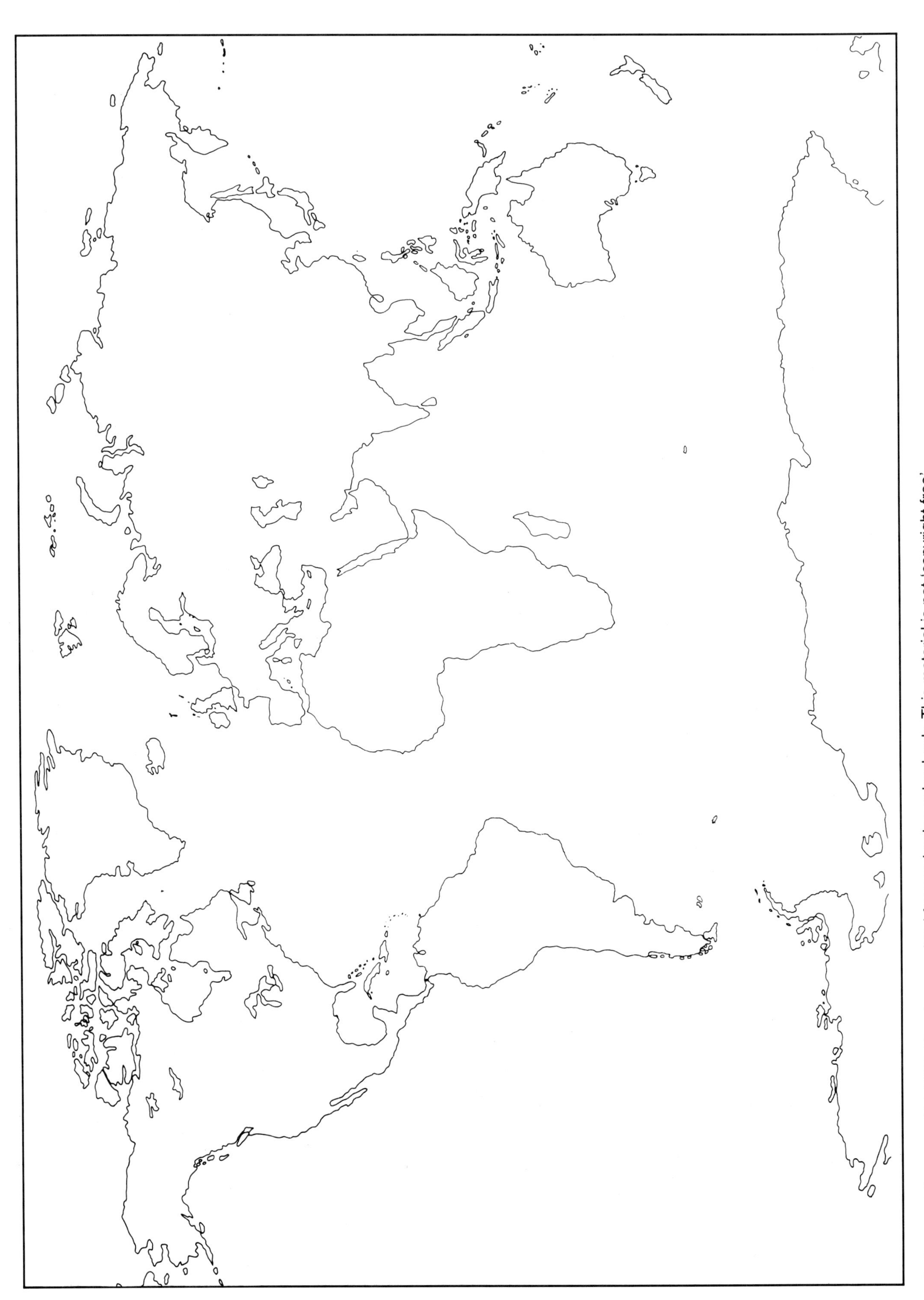

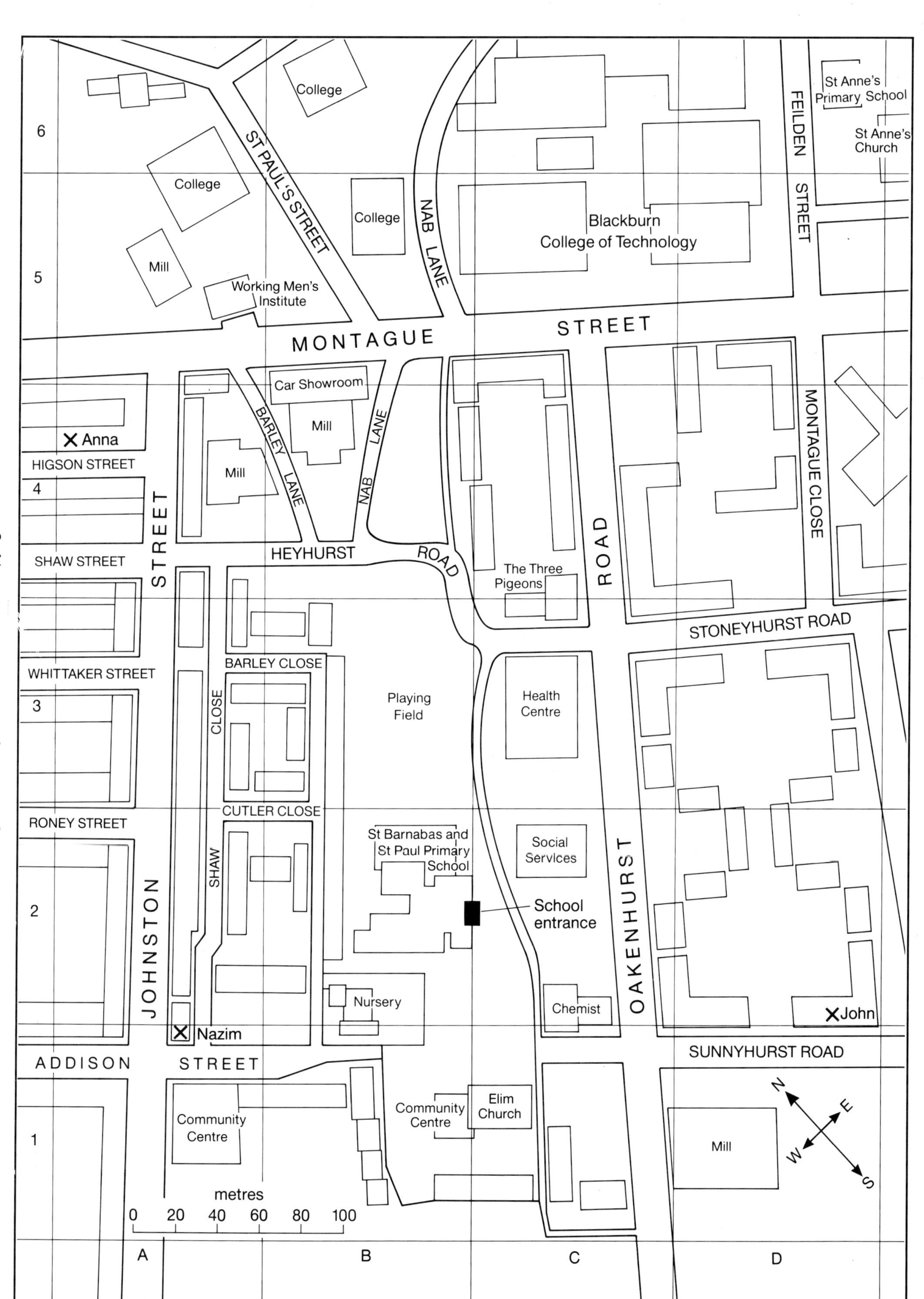
6
5
4
3
2
1
A
B
C
D
College
College
College
Mill
Working Men's Institute
ST PAUL'S STREET
NAB LANE
Blackburn College of Technology
FEILDEN STREET
St Anne's Primary School
St Anne's Church
MONTAGUE STREET
Car Showroom
Mill
Mill
BARLEY LANE
NAB LANE
X Anna
HIGSON STREET
SHAW STREET
WHITTAKER STREET
RONEY STREET
JOHNSTON STREET
HEYHURST ROAD
The Three Pigeons
ROAD
MONTAGUE CLOSE
STONEYHURST ROAD
BARLEY CLOSE
CLOSE
Playing Field
Health Centre
CUTLER CLOSE
SHAW
St Barnabas and St Paul Primary School
Social Services
School entrance
OAKENHURST
Nursery
Chemist
X John
X Nazim
ADDISON STREET
SUNNYHURST ROAD
Community Centre
Community Centre
Elim Church
Mill
N
E
W
S
metres
0 20 40 60 80 100

Map of St Abbs

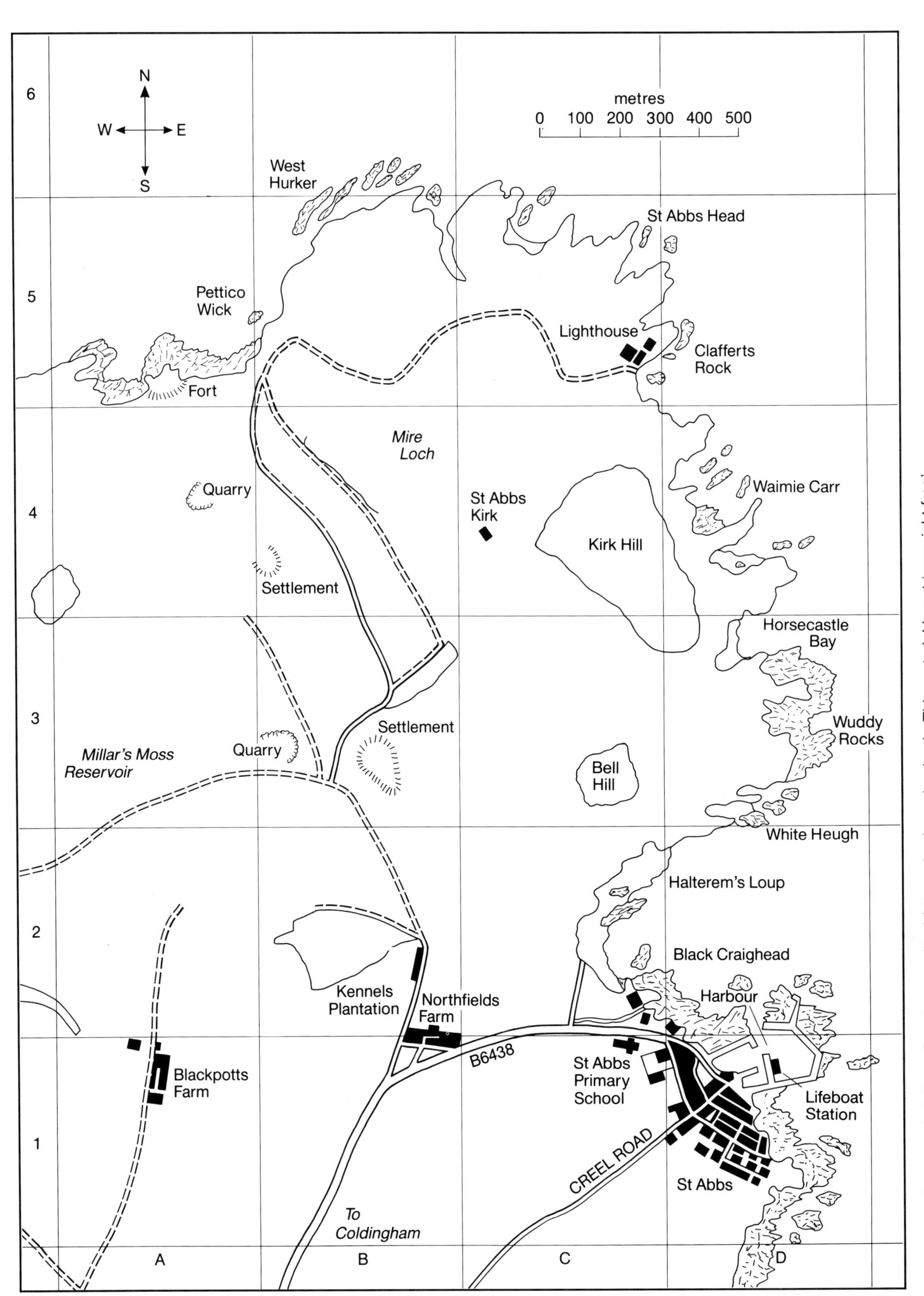

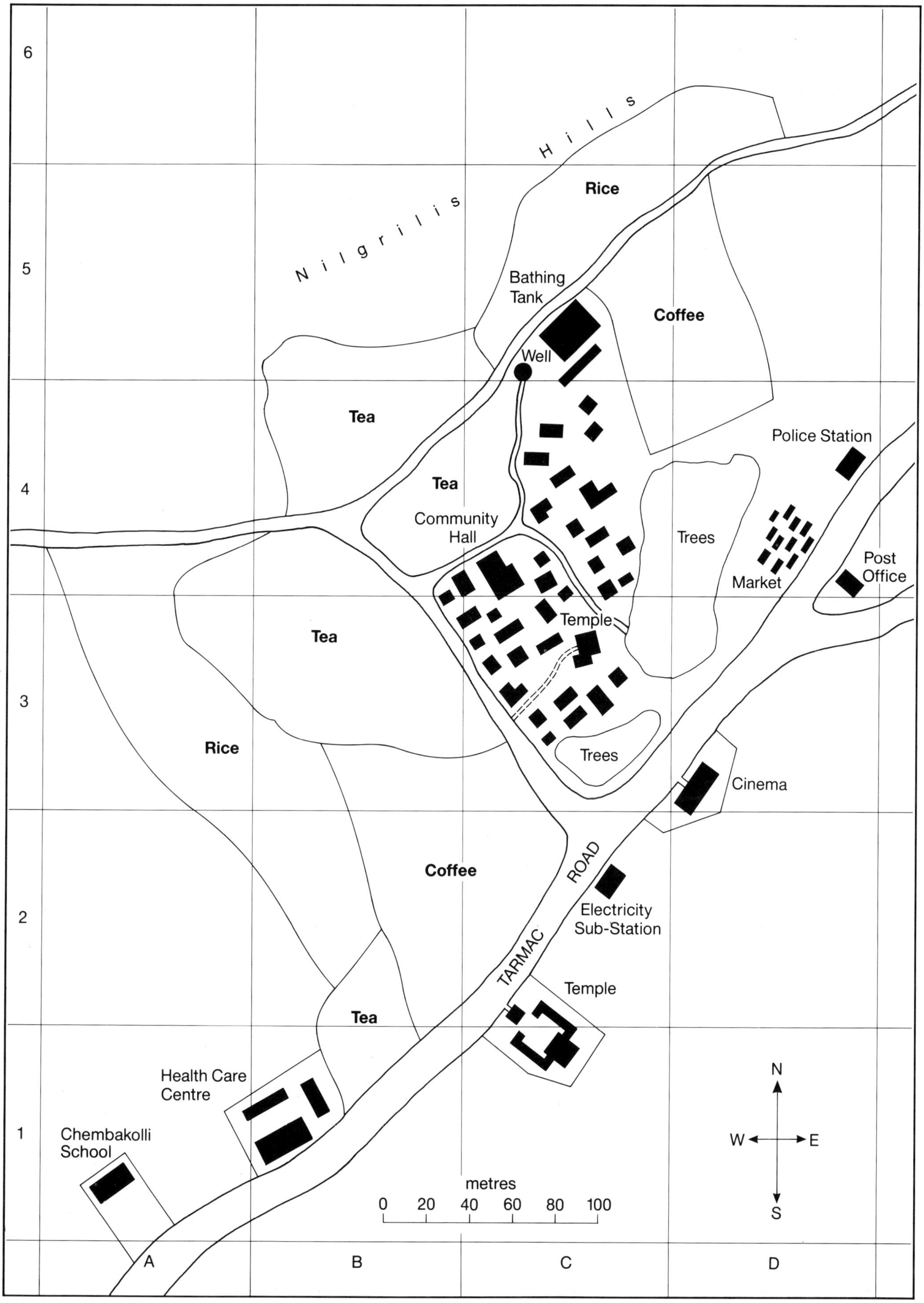

Map of Chembakolli

Nilgrilis Hills
Rice
Bathing Tank
Coffee
Well
Tea
Tea
Police Station
Community Hall
Trees
Market
Post Office
Temple
Tea
Rice
Trees
Cinema
Coffee
TARMAC ROAD
Electricity Sub-Station
Temple
Tea
Health Care Centre
Chembakolli School
metres
0 20 40 60 80 100
N
W E
S
6
5
4
3
2
1
A B C D

Can you put these in the right order?

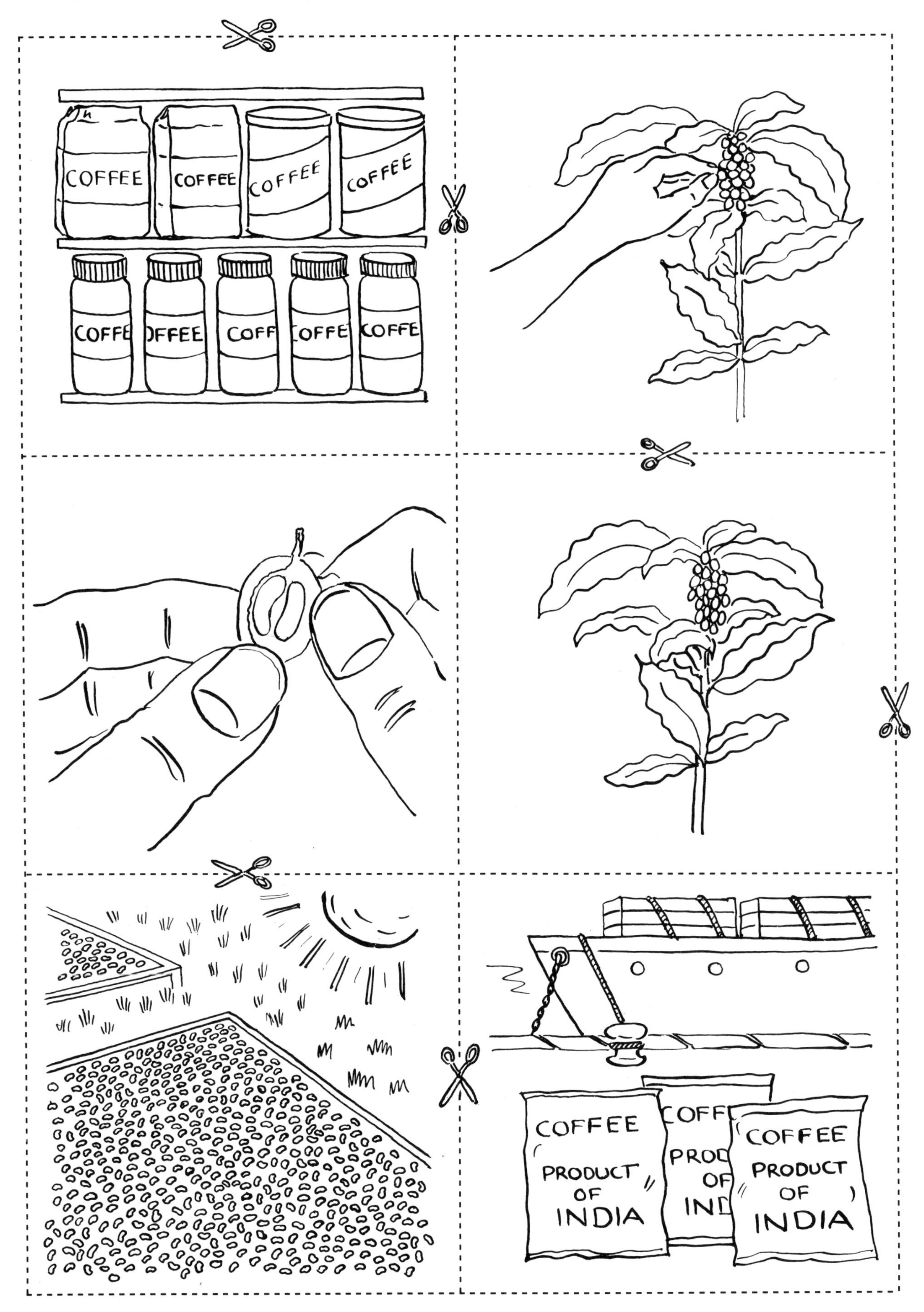

Write and draw pictures about life in these places.

	BLACKBURN	ST ABBS	CHEMBAKOLLI
 School			
 Homes			
 Land use			

Plan of retail park

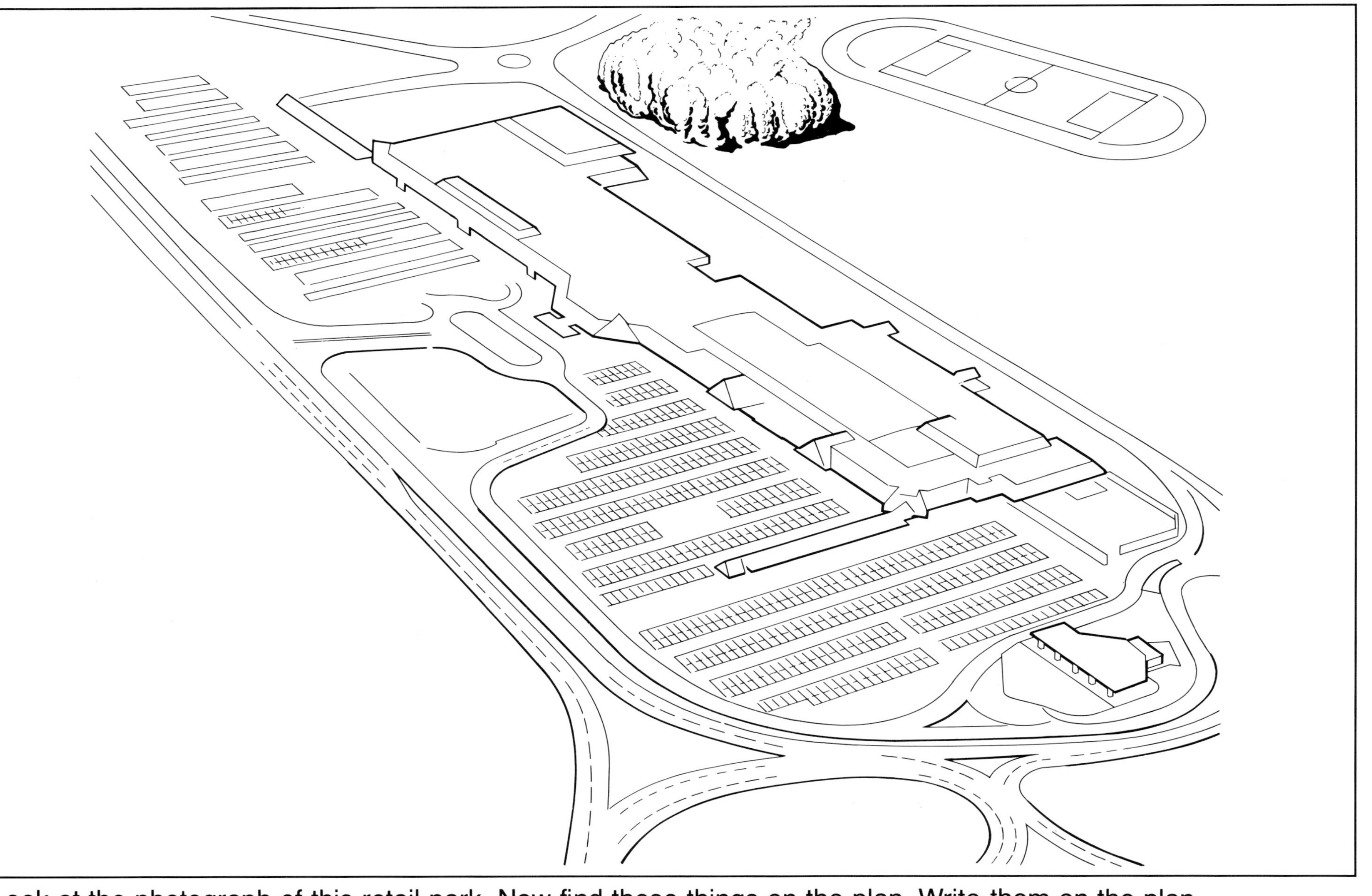

Look at the photograph of this retail park. Now find these things on the plan. Write them on the plan.

car park   woods   superstores   sports field   roads   petrol station

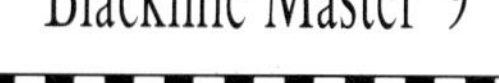

Plan of Caldbeck

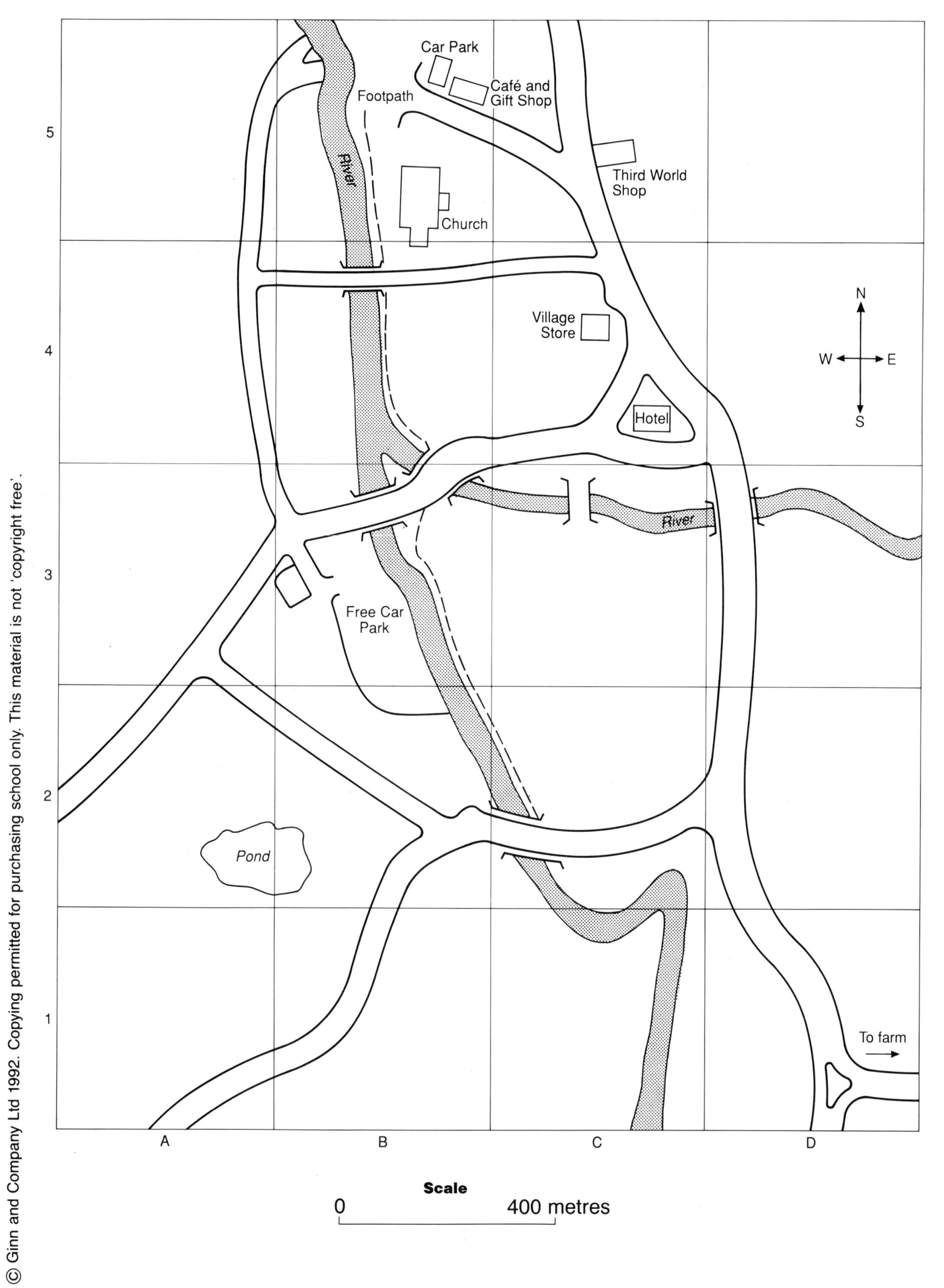

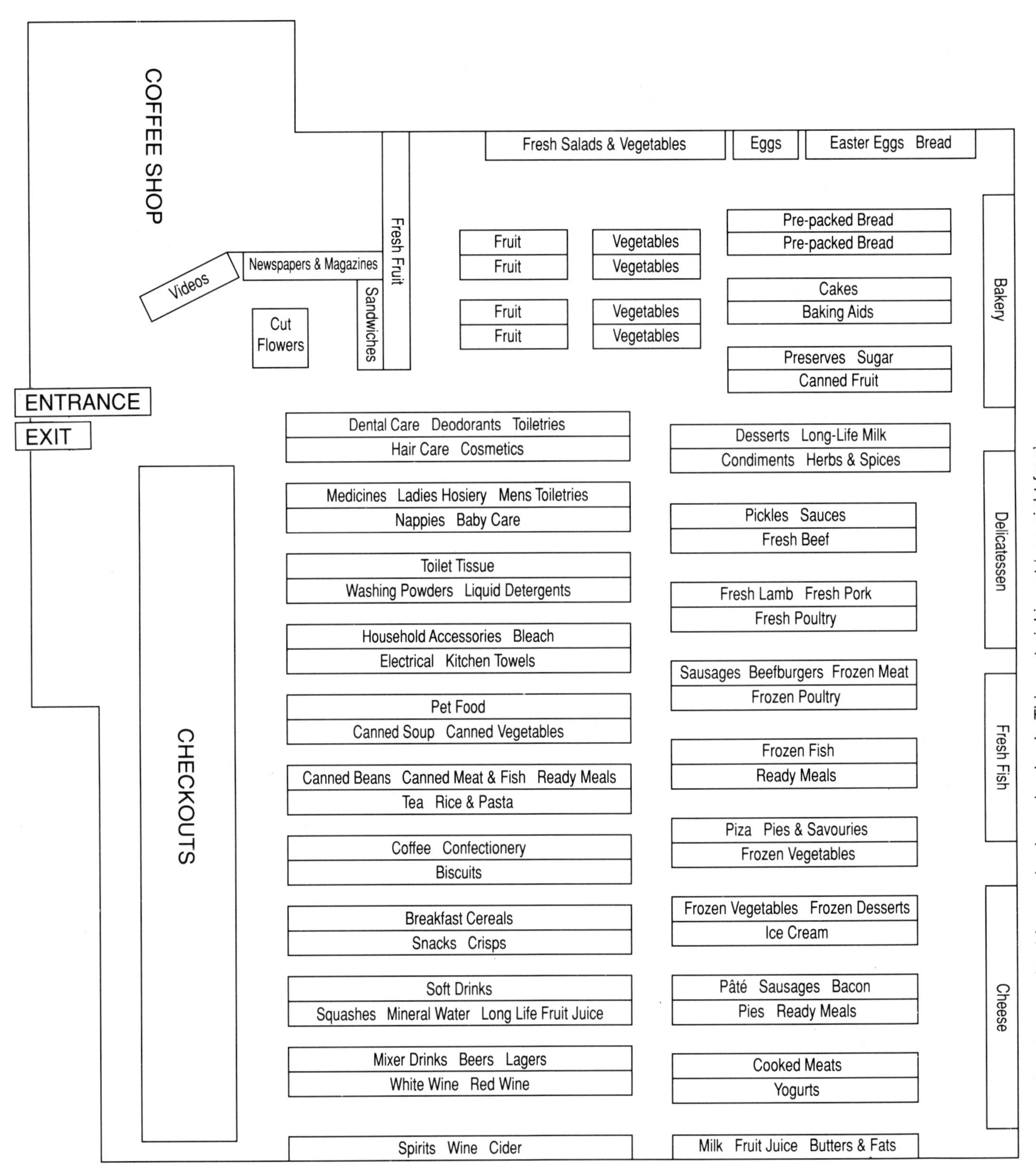
COFFEE SHOP
Fresh Salads & Vegetables
Eggs
Easter Eggs Bread
Fresh Fruit
Newspapers & Magazines
Videos
Sandwiches
Cut Flowers
Fruit
Fruit
Fruit
Fruit
Vegetables
Vegetables
Vegetables
Vegetables
Pre-packed Bread
Pre-packed Bread
Cakes
Baking Aids
Preserves Sugar
Canned Fruit
Bakery
ENTRANCE
EXIT
Dental Care Deodorants Toiletries
Hair Care Cosmetics
Desserts Long-Life Milk
Condiments Herbs & Spices
Delicatessen
Medicines Ladies Hosiery Mens Toiletries
Nappies Baby Care
Pickles Sauces
Fresh Beef
Toilet Tissue
Washing Powders Liquid Detergents
Fresh Lamb Fresh Pork
Fresh Poultry
Household Accessories Bleach
Electrical Kitchen Towels
Sausages Beefburgers Frozen Meat
Frozen Poultry
Pet Food
Canned Soup Canned Vegetables
Fresh Fish
CHECKOUTS
Frozen Fish
Ready Meals
Canned Beans Canned Meat & Fish Ready Meals
Tea Rice & Pasta
Piza Pies & Savouries
Frozen Vegetables
Coffee Confectionery
Biscuits
Frozen Vegetables Frozen Desserts
Ice Cream
Breakfast Cereals
Snacks Crisps
Cheese
Soft Drinks
Squashes Mineral Water Long Life Fruit Juice
Pâté Sausages Bacon
Pies Ready Meals
Mixer Drinks Beers Lagers
White Wine Red Wine
Cooked Meats
Yogurts
Spirits Wine Cider
Milk Fruit Juice Butters & Fats

Store Guide

Which shop does your family visit most often?	
Which days do you visit the shop?	MON / TUES / WED / THUR / FRI / SAT / SUN
How far is the shop from your home?	
How do your family travel there?	car / on foot / bus / train
At what times of day do you usually visit the shop?	
What sorts of things can you buy in the shop?	

Weather map

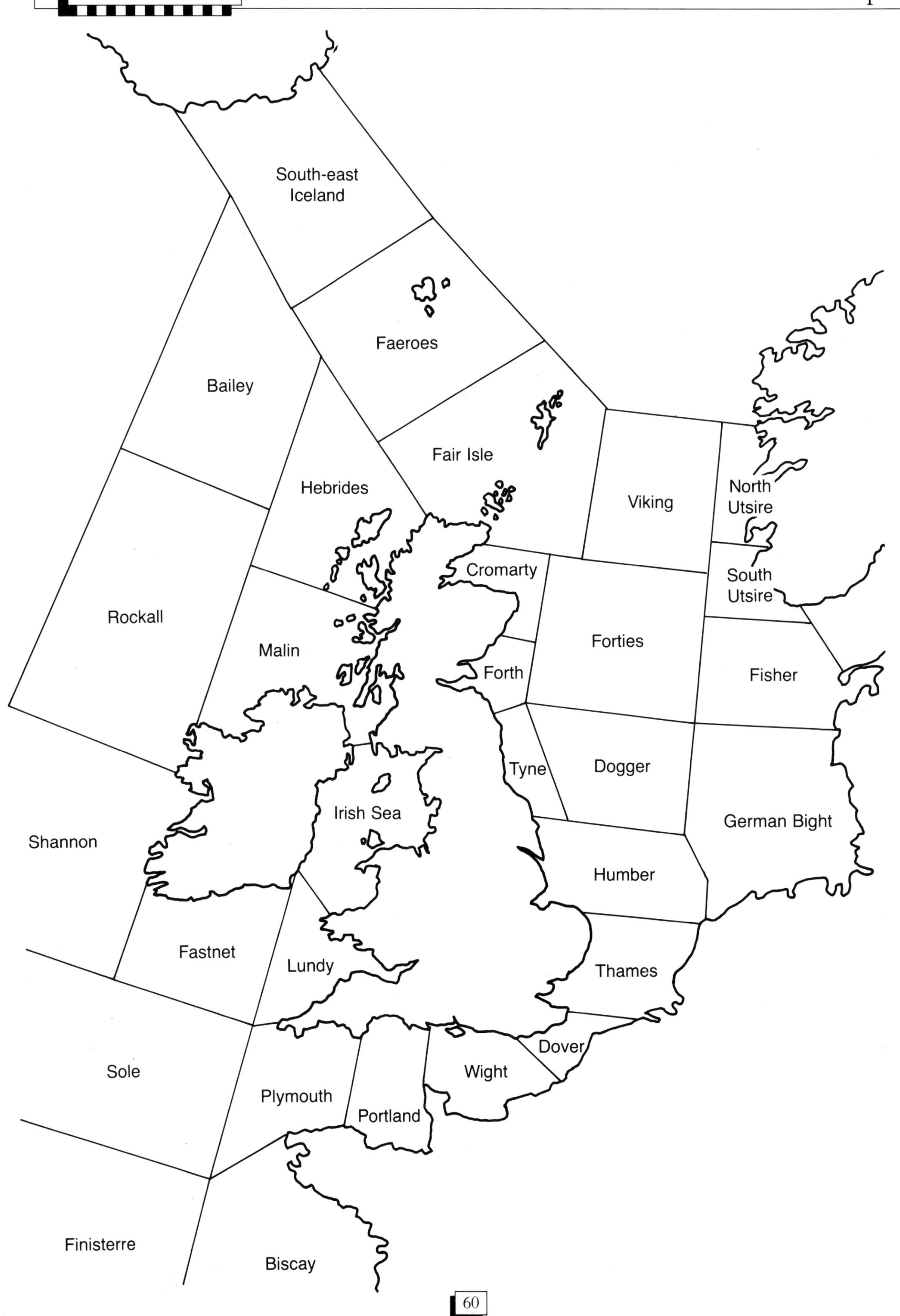
South-east Iceland
Faeroes
Bailey
Fair Isle
Hebrides
Viking
North Utsire
Rockall
Cromarty
South Utsire
Malin
Forties
Forth
Fisher
Tyne
Dogger
Irish Sea
German Bight
Shannon
Humber
Fastnet
Lundy
Thames
Dover
Sole
Wight
Plymouth
Portland
Finisterre
Biscay

 **What will the weather be like tomorrow?** 	
Tomorrow's date	
The hottest place tomorrow in the UK	
The coldest place tomorrow in the UK	
The wettest place tomorrow in the UK	
The driest place tomorrow in the UK	

Weather record

Date			
Place			
Temperature: Ground		Air	
 Amount of rain			
 Direction of the wind			
 Strength of the wind			
 General description of weather			

Sunshine

Rain

Snow

Thunderstorm

Hail

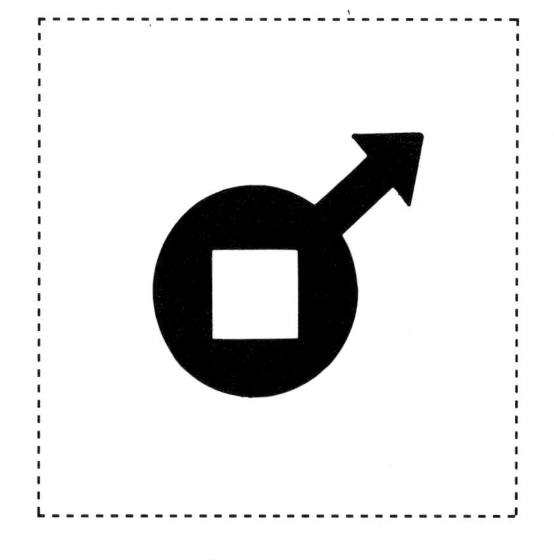

Wind speed

Class: **Planning sheet**

ACTIVITY	RESOURCES	ASSESSMENT	AT